A GLOBAL ISSUES TITLE

BRAVE NEW SEEDS

The Threat of GM Crops to Farmers

Robert Ali Brac de la Perrière
& Franck Seuret

Translated by
Manisha Sovani & Vijaya Rao

Zed Books
LONDON AND NEW YORK

Pluto Press
AUSTRALIA

University Press Ltd
DHAKA

White Lotus Co. Ltd
BANGKOK

Fernwood Publishing Ltd
HALIFAX, NOVA SCOTIA

David Philip
CAPE TOWN

Brave New Seeds: The Threat of Transgenic Crops to Farmers
was first published in 2000 by

In Australasia: Pluto Press Australia, 6A Nelson Street,
Annandale, NSW 2038, Sydney, Australia

In Bangladesh: The University Press Ltd, Red Crescent Building,
114 Motijheel C/A, PO Box 2611, Dhaka 1000

In Burma, Cambodia, Laos, Thailand and Vietnam:
White Lotus Co. Ltd, GPO Box 1141, Bangkok 10501, Thailand.

In Canada: Fernwood Publishing Ltd, PO Box 9409, Station A,
Halifax, Nova Scotia, Canada B3K 5S3

In Southern Africa: David Philip Publishers (Pty Ltd),
208 Werdmuller Centre, Claremont 7735, South Africa

In the rest of the world:
Zed Books Ltd., 7 Cynthia Street, London N1 9JF, UK and
Room 400, 175 Fifth Avenue, New York, NY 10010, USA

Distributed in the USA exclusively by St Martin's Press, Inc.,
175 Fifth Avenue, New York, NY 10010, USA

Copyright © Robert Ali Brac de la Perrière and Franck Seuret, 2000
English language translation © Manisha Sovani and Vijaya Rao, 2000
Cover design by Andrew Corbett
Set in 11/14 pt Monotype Bembo by Long House, Cumbria, UK
Printed and bound in the United Kingdom by Cox & Wyman, Reading

The publishers gratefully acknowledge the role that the Fondation Charles Léopold Mayer pour le Progrès de l'Homme played in facilitating the dialogue with farmers' representatives out of which the text of this book was developed; its translation from French into English; and the publication of the French language edition of this book.

A catalogue record for this book is available from the British Library
US CIP data is available from the Library of Congress
Canadian CIP data is available from the National Library of Canada

ISBN: 1 86403 193 X Pb (Australasia)
ISBN: 1 55266 038 9 Pb (Canada)
ISBN: 0 86486 366 7 Pb (Southern Africa)
ISBN: 1 85649 899 9 Hb (Zed Books)
ISBN: 1 85649 900 6 Pb (Zed Books)

A Brave New Series

GLOBAL ISSUES
IN A CHANGING WORLD

This new series of short, accessible think pieces deals with leading global issues of relevance to humanity today. Intended for the enquiring reader and social activists in the North and the South, as well as students, the books explain what is at stake and question conventional ideas and policies. Drawn from many different parts of the world, the series' authors pay particular attention to the needs and interests of ordinary people, whether living in the rich industrial or the developing countries. They all share a common objective: to help stimulate new thinking and social action in the opening years of the new century.

Global Issues in a Changing World is a joint initiative by Zed Books in collaboration with a number of partner publishers and non-governmental organizations around the world. By working together, we intend to maximize the relevance and availability of the books published in the series.

PARTICIPATING NGOS

- *Both ENDS, Amsterdam*
- *Catholic Institute for International Relations, London*
- *Corner House, Sturminster Newton*
- *Focus on the Global South, Bangkok*
- *Inter Pares, Ottawa*
- *Third World Network, Penang*
- *World Development Movement, London*

*

'Communities in the South are facing great difficulties in coping with global trends. I hope this brave new series will throw much needed light on the issues ahead and help us choose the right options.'
Martin Khor, Director, Third World Network

'There is no more important campaign than our struggle to bring the global economy under democratic control. But the issues are fearsomely complex. This Global Issues Series is a valuable resource for the committed campaigner and the educated citizen.'
Barry Coates, Director, World Development Movement (WDM)

Titles in the Global Issues Series

Autumn 2000

Another American Century?
The United States and the World
after 2000
Nicholas Guyatt

Brave New Seeds
The Threat of GM Crops to Farmers
Robert Ali Brac de la Perrière
and Franck Seuret

Hungry for Trade
How the Poor Pay for Free Trade
John Madeley

Spring 2001

The Myth of Development
An Emergency Agenda
for the Survival of Nations
Oswald de Rivero

The Water Manifesto
Arguments for a
World Water Contract
Riccardo Petrella

IN PREPARATION

Free Market Economics
The Intelligent Person's Guide to
Liberalisation
Amit Bhaduri
and Deepak Nayyar

Trading Development
Trade, Globalisation and Alternative
Development Possibilities
Graham Dunkley

Governing Biotechnology
The Global Biosafety Regime
Calestous Juma

Sustainable Development
A Critical Reintroduction
Lloyd Pettiford

A New Globalism
An Alternative to the
Breakdown of World Order
Harry Shutt

A Level Playing Field
Changing the Rules
of the Global Economy
Oscar Ugarteche

For full details of this list and Zed's other subject and general
catalogues, please write to: The Marketing Department, Zed Books, 7 Cynthia Street,
London N1 9JF, UK or email Sales@zedbooks.demon.co.uk

Visit our website at: http:/www.zedbooks.demon.co.uk

CONTENTS

ABOUT THE AUTHORS

Robert Ali Brac de la Perrière is an international consultant. With a doctorate in plant breeding, he specialises in the organisation, training and mangement of plant genetic resource programmes for the development of *in situ* conservation activities. He has extensive experience in managing interdisciplinary consultations and organising colloquia between NGOs and scientific institutions, particularly in the Mediterranean and African regions.

Franck Seuret is a journalist. After working with peasants in Niger in the mid-1990s, he began to write for various French magazines, specialising in rural development, economic issues in developing countries and biotechnology.

ABOUT THIS BOOK

'This unique gathering of scientists, farmers and development specialists has given us an impressively cogent summary of the hazards of GMOs and the urgency of worldwide action. *Brave New Seeds* embraces the central contributions of southern farmers to the integrity of our food and the diversity of world agriculture. It illustrates the failure of commodity-centered development models, and reaffirms the necessity of returning the control over seeds to farmers, as the true agricultural innovators and the real custodians of sustainability.' – **Brian Tokar,** Editor, *Redesigning Life? The Worldwide Challenge to Genetic Engineering*

'Seeds belong to farmers – the discoverers, selectors and protectors of humanity's agricultural biodiversity for the past eight millennia. The present push by big business to enslave farmers and put both their livelihoods and the very existence of humankind in peril needs to be exposed and brought to the notice of all sectors of society, but particularly the farmers, both big and small.

This book by Robert Ali Brac de la Perrière and Franck Seuret is very timely in informing the key actors. The authors are particularly to be congratulated for putting farmers first in this debate and providing a clear explanation of the several terms and phrases being used by media policy makers and scientists.' – **Tewolde Berhan Gebre Egziabher,** *spokesperson for the 'Like Minded Group' in the negotiations of the Cartagena Protocol on Safety in Biotechnology.*

ACKNOWLEDGEMENTS

This document is based on points discussed during the international seminar co-organised by the Charles Léopold Mayer Foundation for the Progress of Humankind and Disha, a rural development social organisation, which took place during 5–10 December 1998 on the banks of the Ganges in Uttar Pradesh, India.

First we thank the members of Disha and their director K. N. Tiwari, who welcomed our highly atypical microcosm with warmth and simplicity. For a week, the Garhwal Mandal Vikas Nigam of Rishikesh became the intercontinental inn for a reconciled humanity.

We acknowledge Dhum Singh Negi, Kunwar Prasun and Vijay Jardhari and reaffirm our admiration for the fight led by Beej Bachao Andolan – the Save the Seeds movement. These activists accompanied us throughout the seminar, debated on the Terminator transgenic varieties, took us to visit their farming land in the foothills of the Himalayas, and led us on a discovery of the extraordinary diversity of rice and pulse that they are preserving. The meal and the exchange we enjoyed with the women farmers of Tehri Garhwal, true guardians of agricultural diversity, will remain an enduring memory for a number of participants.

Bharat Dogra, Madhu and their daughter were responsible for the success of this event. Their experienced preparations, their discreet and warm presence, and the fineness of their ministrations made them excellent hosts and very efficient coordinators.

Hats off to the initial mediators, Alliance for a Responsible and United World in Dehra Dun, who are so adept at reducing the world to a village – as they enthusiastically proved during this unique week of intercontinental exchange in Rishikesh. To Sarfaraz Khan and Nacera Aknak-Khan, to Philippe Guirlet and Nadia Leila Aissaoui, and to Simron Jit Singh, many thanks for your welcome before, during and after the meeting, all along the way.

Arnaud Trollé, Carine Pionetti, Jacques Mirenowicz, Dominique

Louette, Arnaud Apoteker and Bharat Dogra kept minutes of the meetings, and their meticulous reports were extremely useful in restoring the richness of the debates.

Our very special thanks to Manisha Sovani and Vijaya Rao, the translators of the seminar, for their extraordinary patience and avail-ability. So often the major responsibility for the inter-cultural dialogue rested on their shoulders.

Finally, a big thank you to Isabelle Tarradellas, and the INI pro-gramme of the Charles Léopold Mayer Foundation for their unwaver-ing support in this remarkable adventure.

ABBREVIATIONS

APM	Agriculture Peasant and Modernisation
ASPTA	Assessoria e Serviços a Projeto em Agricultura Alternativa
CBD	Convention on Biological Diversity
CGIAR	Consultative Group on International Agricultural Research
CINVESTAV	Centre of Research and Advanced Studies (National Polytechnic Institute, Mexico)
CTDT	Community Technology Development Trust
DUS	Distinctive character, uniformity and stability
ERMURS	Equipe de recherche sur les mutations du rural sahélien
FAO	Food and Agriculture Organisation
FPH	Charles Léopold Mayer Foundation for the Progress of Humankind
GE	Genetic engineering
GMO	Genetically modified organism
GRAIN	Genetic Resources Action International
IATP	Institute for Agriculture and Trade Policy
IFA	International Forum on Food and Agriculture
IFG	International Forum on Globalisation
IMECBIO	Manantlan Institute of Ecology and Conservation of Biodiversity
INRA	L'Institut National de Recherche Agronomique
IPGRI	International Phytogenetics Resources Institute
IPR	Intellectual property rights
IRRI	International Rice Research Institute
JPP	Jajarkot Permaculture Programme
KRRS	Karnataka Rajia Ryota Sougha (Karnataka State Farmers' Association)

MASIPAG	Farmer–Scientist Partnership for Development
NGO	Non-governmental organisation
OAPI	Organisation Africaine de la Propriété Intellectuelle
OAU	Organisation for African Unity
OECD	Organisation for Economic Cooperation and Development
RAFI	Rural Advancement Foundation International
RIAD	Red Interamericana Agricultura y Democratia
SIRDC	Scientific Industrial Research and Development Centre
UCS	Union of Concerned Scientists
UNIDO	United Nations Industrial Development Organisation
UPOV	Union for the Protection of New Varieties of Plants
WIPO	World Intellectual Property Organisation
WTO	World Trade Organisation

INTRODUCTION

Four thousand years of history are being obliterated and will soon be forgotten. It is 4,000 years since the beginning of Indian agriculture or, more precisely, the first cultivation of the main cereals in India; 4,000 years during which billions of Indian farmers have laboured together in a gigantic task, the diversification of vegetal varieties. Each generation contributed its mite: crossing one variety with another; selecting the best-adapted varieties; constantly improving techniques for a sustainable agriculture, respectful of land and life. Then, thirty years ago, a spoke was placed in this precious wheel. In the name of progress and the necessity for increased yields, the Green Revolution enforced a mode of agriculture that had high-yield varieties, fertilisers and pesticides as its new gods. Gradually, many Indian farmers abandoned the principles of sustainable agriculture and converted to intensive agriculture, relegating four millennia of experience to the limbo of history.

All that for a revolution that did not live up to its promises. The number of hectares cultivated increased; but productivity, which rose in the initial years, progressively declined. The consumption of fertilisers and pesticides increased enormously and the number of varieties cultivated dropped sharply. In short, the balance sheet does not look good. Yet this movement for uniformity of cultivation is going to accelerate even further with the arrival in full force of GMOs, genetically modified organisms, whose genetic heritage has been modified to give them new properties: tolerance to a herbicide, or resistance to an insect or to the cold. This second Green Revolution threatens to carry away all that remains of the fabulous vegetal

1

heritage gathered down the ages by Indian farmers, imposing instead a single standard of transgenic plants.

The seed savers

Certain groups of agriculturists like the Save the Seeds movement in India have been working for years to safeguard traditional varieties. 'The Save the Seeds movement was created towards the late 1980s by several farmers including Vijay Jardhari, a farmer in the Tehri Garhwal region who was worried about the undesirable effects of the intensive use of chemical products on his lands,' relates Bharat Dogra, an Indian journalist who devoted a book to the roots of resistance in Indian rural organisations.[1]

> After some hesitation, he and his wife Kamla decided not to grow the new chemical-dependent seeds on their farms. This was not an easy decision to make. Like most hill farmers of this region, the Jardhari family barely manages to make ends meet. The new Green Revolution was attracting more and more farmers by promising higher yields in quick time. To make this offer even more attractive, extension agents were distributing free chemical fertilisers and seeds during the initial period. The temptation of taking the new seeds and abandoning the old was too great for many farmers to resist. But Vijay persuaded himself and his family members that the rapid spread of this new technology in the villages was precisely the reason for someone to try and conserve the traditional seeds.

Since then, Vijay Jardhari and like-minded companions have continued to grow and preserve traditional seeds on their farms. And they are not alone. In the high valley of Ramasirin in the Uttarkashi region, for instance, they found farmers who were cultivating a rice variety called Chardhan, so well adapted to local conditions that they adamantly refused to convert to the high-yield variety of the Green Revolution. In other villages, the seed savers also identified rice varieties (Thapachini, Jhumkiya and Lal Basmati) which could claim yields comparable to the new varieties, the only difference being that the former could be cultivated without chemical fertilisers or pesticides whereas the latter absolutely needed these technological crutches.

One day, a visiting scientist asked them ironically, 'If your Thapachini variety is so good, why don't you grow it everywhere?', relates Bharat Dogra. Vijay Jardhari replied 'that each variety has its own role for specific farm conditions and so a wide diversity of crops is needed, not monoculture.'

More than ten years after beginning its meticulous work of preservation, the Save the Seeds movement is on the path to success. Bharat Dogra reports that a large number of farmers are now coming forward with requests for seeds.

So far, nearly 130 varieties of rice, nearly 150 varieties of kidney beans, as well as other varieties of several crops have been conserved.... However, the very difficult conditions in which all these farmers and activists are working imposes constraints on how many farmers they can reach to tell them about their work and the importance of conserving traditional seeds.

Informing the communities of the South

The story of the Save the Seeds movement perfectly illustrates the fight led by the farmers who are resistant to the dogma of intensive agriculture and the programmed invasion of GMOs. It is therefore naturally at Rishikesh, the city closest to the 'resistant' villages, that the Charles Léopold Mayer Foundation for the Progress of Humankind (FPH), a Swiss foundation that supports initiatives for producing and spreading knowledge to those who have least access, and Disha, an Indian association for rural development in Uttar Pradesh, chose to organise a seminar on the theme 'Biodiversity, rights of rural communities and the implications of genetically modified organisms'.[2] About fifty people from Asia, America, Africa and Europe met for five days (5–10 December 1998) in this sacred city by the Ganges, in North India, for an unusual international meeting. Its sessions did not take place in luxurious settings but in a modest hotel with rustic charm. Side by side in a circle, seated on mats around French–English–Hindi interpreters, participants from all horizons met – farmers and scientists, representatives of rural organisations and members of environmental protection associations – for a multicultural debate.

The Rishikesh seminar completed a cycle of three meetings on the implications of genetically modified organisms for the agricultural world, consumers and civilians. The first took place in November 1997 in Switzerland and concerned the Swiss referendum on their opposition to GMOs.[3] The second, which took place in Brussels (Belgium) in April 1998, placed an emphasis on changes that the arrival of GMOs provoked in agricultural research and sustainable research in Europe.[4] The Rishikesh seminar had a triple objective: to reinforce the capacity for rural communities of the South to understand the implications of GMOs, to promote their involvement in the debate and to contribute to the installation of an information network on this subject.

Rural societies in developing countries are unprepared for the onslaught of this biotechnological revolution. The majority of farmers in the Asian and African countryside have no knowledge of transgenic plants. Certainly, a lot of rural organisations like Save the Seeds have fought hard against the obliteration of agricultural biodiversity in India (Rupantar, KRRS), just as other NGOs have in the Philippines (MASIPAG), in Thailand (Biothai) or in South America (ASPTA, RIAD). But today these associations have to confront a new challenge: the arrival of GMOs. The priority therefore is to spread the word rapidly and widely about a complex and high-risk subject that is threatening traditional agricultural systems. Many other meetings like Rishikesh are needed. Soon after this Indian seminar, two other information workshops were organised: the first at Saharanpur in India by Disha and the second in Nepal by the Permaculture Programme of Jajarkot.

This book takes into account the work that went into and the conclusions that emerged from five Indian days. An unusual seminar deserves an unusual book. *Brave New Seeds* does not simply recapitulate the contributions of the different participants, one after the other. Instead it offers a scenario of the implications of the introduction of GMOs in developing countries. This 'file for debate', which has been translated into Hindi for Indian farmers, will contribute towards the collective reflection that began at Rishikesh by drawing the attention of the participants to the most pertinent texts on the subject. The authors have tried to retain the objectives of the meeting: to warn rural communities against the consequences of using transgenic varieties in their agriculture and to facilitate their access to information that will enable them to conduct the fight. We hope that we have not misinterpreted the words of the participants in this recomposition. We alone assume responsibility for the final text.

The Rishikesh Declaration

Brave New Seeds has been divided into seven chapters, each taking up points from the final declaration adopted by the participants in the Rishikesh seminar.

Principles

Five principles are the foundation of sustainable agriculture and peaceful debate on genetically modified organisms:

1 Seeds belong to farmers and not to corporations. Farmers have always protected the broad biodiversity of their fields.
2 We should clearly say 'No' to terminator technology and all related technologies that aim at preventing a seed from germinating when replanted.
3 Considering the highly hazardous nature of GMO technology, controlled by a few multinational companies, it is imperative to exercise the greatest caution in trials and experiments involving GMOs. The health rights of consumers should be adequately protected.
4 We note with concern that much work relating to GMOs has been shrouded in secrecy and misinformation. We call for complete transparency on the part of governments as well as corporations on all issues concerning GMOs. Considering the high hazard potential of GMOs, accountability for the risks associated with GMOs should be clearly established.
5 Broader questions need to be raised about the ethics of science in relation to greater risks of new hazards, as well as development processes that imply the unregulated proliferation of these hazards.

Means of action

To safeguard the interests of farmers and local communities:

1 A moratorium should be imposed on the commercialisation of GMOs until it has been proved that they have no detrimental effects on environment and health. If any GMOs are commercialised, after satisfying all safety norms, it should be ensured that they reinforce true food security and sustainable agricultural systems.

2 The rights of farming communities should be fully protected within the framework of the WTO's agreement on Trade Related Aspects of Intellectual Property Rights (TRIPS). These rights should include the rights of farmers as innovators and preservers of seeds.

3 When amending patent laws in accordance with the TRIPS Agreement, provisions of section 2 of Article 27 of the TRIPS Agreement can be used as it allows members to 'exclude from patentability, any invention that might be perceived as detrimental to public order and morality if commercialised on their territory. This includes any threat to human, animal and plant safety or serious prejudice to the environment…'.

Notes

1 Bharat Dogra, *Our Fields, Our Seeds: Farmers' Self-reliance and Protection of Land Will Help Struggle against Hunger* (Bharat Dogra, C-27, Raksha Kunj, Paschim Vihar, New Delhi 110063, India, 1998), 40 pages.
2 Seminar organised by the association Disha in collaboration with Save the Seeds movement and Bharat Dogra, an Indian journalist.
3 *Aliments transgéniques: des craintes révélatrices – sous la direction de Robert Ali Brac de la Perrière et Arnaud Trollé* (Charles Léopold Mayer Publications, 1998).
4 Robert Ali Brac de la Perrière and Arnaud Trollé, *The Transgenic Trap? On Bridging Research and Agriculture* (Charles Léopold Mayer Publications, 1999).

1

SEEDS BELONG TO FARMERS
The Downside of GM Seeds for Agriculture in the South

'Seeds belong to farmers and not to corporations. Farmers have always protected the broad biodiversity of their fields.'

Monsanto did not invent anything.[1] For centuries, farmers all over the world have been improving plant varieties. Yet today the biotechnological giant Monsanto and others claim a monopoly on plant breeding, not directly but through patents and transgenic seeds. They sell very expensive seeds which require heavy agricultural inputs. Worse, the farmer has no right to reuse them for further sowing or cross-breeding. After the green revolution, it is the genetic revolution that may engender a new wave of intensified agriculture and the programmed elimination of millions of small farmers. The effects are bound to be especially harsh in countries of the southern hemisphere where farming is an extensive activity involving many more people than it does in industrialised countries.

Long years of breeding work by farmers

Seeds belong to farmers. It would appear that this idea needs to be constantly reiterated and explained, since the multinationals that create transgenic plants have a tendency to forget that the varieties cultivated today are the result of slow and steady breeding by farmers the world over for centuries. 'Most of the plants cultivated are from the South where the farmers have been breeding, maintaining and preserving agricultural diversity for many thousands of years,' say GRAIN (Genetic Resources Action International) and the Gaia Foundation (NGOs which are fighting against the erosion of agricultural diversity) in one of their publications.[2] 'Their work proved to be one of the most significant contributions to the biodiversity of our planet. The story of the plant varieties that we are cultivating and consuming today could be described as the longest and most innovative research project in human history.' Farmers and their fields make up the oldest research team in the world. 'Diversity in agriculture is the result of sustained interactions between farmers and their environment', emphasises Carine Pionetti, a French–Canadian ethnologist and author of a study on biodiversity in India.[3] 'By observing, experimenting and innovating, they developed agricultural practices suitable to the local ecosystems and bred varieties that were capable of surviving in specific terrain and climates.' It is farmers who created, over many generations, the wealth of varieties that we use today. It is they who domesticated, bred and crossed existing varieties in order to obtain new varieties best suited to our needs. It is they again who, after each season, preserved a part of the seeds obtained in order to sow them again. They have provided us with this invaluable heritage today.

But the genetic revolution is changing the present order. Henceforth, it is the industrialists who are claiming a monopoly over plant improvement with new methods whose cost and technical nature make them inaccessible to farmers. 'Transgenesis involves a set of extremely complex and expensive scientific techniques,' states Arnaud Apoteker, who is in charge of the biodiversity programme of Greenpeace France.

> It is impossible for farmers and even small seed producers to take up such activities, which, therefore, remain the prerogative of large multinational companies that are becoming fewer and fewer in number but more and more powerful.... It is no longer international public institutions which hold the reigns of this agricultural revolution, as was the case with the Green revolution. On the contrary, it is the private multinational industries, governed by their commercial interests and necessarily more concerned with possibilities of quick returns, that control it.

The privatisation of life

To ensure returns on their investments, these seed companies are claiming exclusive intellectual property rights on plant breeding (see Chapter 7). We are only at the beginning of a gigantic privatisation process that is taking place at world level. Already a part, though very small, of the plant heritage has fallen into the hands of private operators. 'In the guise of protecting biodiversity, seed companies are drawing up an inventory of the living resources used in agriculture or present in the wildest ecosystems.' This was the charge made in a communiqué to arouse public opinion issued by a cluster of French associations fighting for environment protection, farmers' organisations and international unity and aid organisations.[4] 'Plants and micro-organisms are all very quickly patented, genetically manipulated and marketed. All that remains for the inhabitants of the areas where these living beings originated is a pretty catalogue of the resources that they could have one day managed and used for their own benefit. In addition, they have to pay royalties on the cultivars which do not belong to them any longer'. Thus the intricate work of centuries is ripped from its sustaining matrix. 'For these life sciences companies, life is just raw material, a set of genes that one can assemble like a robot,' as Arnaud Apoteker points out.

> They become another invention that is patented just like any other mechanical process. Biotechnology companies are rushing into patenting living beings, micro-organisms, plants, animals, even human cell lines, despite national laws which exclude patenting of living beings. The WTO and the US support these multinationals and are trying to impose patenting on the rest of the world, which will finally give a handful of companies almost full monopoly on genetic resources by limiting the access of farmers who, in fact, have been their guardians for thousands of years [see 'Outcry about Biopiracy', pp. 20-1]. The scope of patents is also becoming wider : Agracetus, for example, has a patent which covers all genetic modifications of the cotton plant and another one on soya. This leads to a number of legal disputes and encourages the concentration of companies in the sector, a number of which are bought out by multinationals, more for their portfolio of patents than their profits. It also causes food insecurity and a concentration of power with the new owners of germplasm'.

This power is concentrated in the hands of a few giants whose reach knows no limits. Some industrial groups have expanded in the past few years through mergers and acquisitions in order to appropriate a large portfolio of intellectual property rights, thereby becoming masters of production and controllers of large agro-food sectors. 'Big multinational agro seed companies are buying up small seed companies that might work against their interests,' states Peter Muchambo, spokesperson for a network of African farmers' organisations known as Agriculture Peasant and Modernisation, Africa (APM Africa) in Zimbabwe. 'Monsanto has been on a shopping spree, buying up Cargill's international seed division, Delta and Pine and others, and thus it has become the world's number two seed company in a very short time.'

Today a few giants – Monsanto (USA), AstraZeneca (GB/Sweden), Novartis (Switzerland), DuPont/Pioneer (USA), Aventis (a merger between Germany's Hoechst, France's Rhône-Poulenc and AgrEvo, a joint subsidiary of Hoechst and Schiering), and DowElanco (USA) – control almost 100 per cent of the transgenic seeds market. The concentration process has certainly not ended. It would not be surprising if their quasi-monopoly were to end as a world-wide game that put the situation of farmers in danger. 'The way world events are unfolding, we might perhaps witness a merger of Pioneer and Monsanto, further aggravating the monopoly situation,' says a concerned Peter Muchambo. 'This will mean that prices will be dictated by them, not farmers.'

Further economic dependence

The development of GMOs will lead to additional costs for farmers in countries of the South. They will be forced to buy genetically modified seeds instead of the 'traditional' seeds they have been using until now. This was the concern of Fred Zinanga, agronomist from the Community Technology Development Trust (Zimbabwe), an NGO fighting for the rights of rural communities, who cited the example of his country.

A review of cotton production in Zimbabwe shows that 70 per cent of the total crop produced annually comes from the small-scale farming sector. As these farmers can barely afford inputs, the crop is normally grown on advances from the cotton companies, which are later deducted at the end of the season. The question is, how would these small-scale farmers be able to afford the purchase of transgenic seeds, especially those with the Bt gene that have to be purchased annually? Monsanto is pushing hard to introduce this crop in Zimbabwe without going through the normal procedures of testing the technology and studying its economic compatibility with the local farming system.... It is therefore highly suicidal to encourage farmers to cultivate the supposedly lucrative transgenic crops, since their seeds are beyond their means.... How will small-scale farmers in future be able to buy new generations of genetically modified seeds, when they already have difficulty in affording certified seeds from the market?

This question becomes all the more pertinent since the farmer who starts using GMOs will have to renew his stocks every year. Seed companies forbid farmers through a contract from storing a part of the grains harvested for sowing in the next season. In June 1998, Monsanto released this warning in American newspapers:

when a farmer stores and sows biotech seeds (genetically modified seeds) patented by Monsanto, he should understand that he is in the wrong. This holds true even if he has not signed any contract at the time of procuring seeds (that is, if he recycles or if he buys seeds illegally from a neighbour). He is pirating.... Moreover, this pirating of seeds could cost the farmer hundreds of dollars per acre by way of damages, interest and legal costs, apart from having to undergo the inspection of his fields and records over many years.[5]

Very soon, this multinational will no longer need to publish such a warning. Thanks to Terminator, it can in the next few years replace, to its advantage, 'contractual' sterility with biological sterility. This new technology of 'controlling gene expression' makes it possible to introduce a sterilising gene in the genotype. The plant develops normally but produces a biologically sterile grain (see Chapter 2). 'The latest discovery in the seed business is the development of plant varieties that are unable to reproduce – dubbed 'terminator technology' – with which they are assured of selling new seeds to farmers each and every year,' says Neil Ritchie, National Organiser for Food and Agriculture Policy at the Institute for Agriculture and Trade Policy (IATP), an organisation that closely studies the evolution of the international policy in the field of food, environment and biotechnology. 'But for inhabitants of countries that are subject to problems of food security, this is a deadly invention. Especially since it is known that these transgenic plants require specific chemical treatment.'

Most of the genetically modified seeds – 70 per cent according to the Rural Advancement Foundation International (RAFI), an NGO fighting for the conservation and sustainable use of agricultural biodiversity – contain a gene that is resistant to a particular herbicide. Farmers are then forced to buy this chemical product because of which they incur extra costs in addition to that of the seeds. 'Some GMOs may perhaps reduce the consumption of chemical pesticides but most transgenic products are designed for resistance to herbicides sold by the same multinationals,' say Greenpeace and other associations.[6]

> Globally, the biotechnology solution imposes an increased dependence on inputs. This tendency increases intensive monoculture and steadily marginalises small-scale farmers who are already the most vulnerable to hunger.

Programmed elimination of small farmers

This is the basis of the whole problem: GMOs pave the way for a new intensified agriculture which will result in the weakening and elimination of small-scale farmers. 'The complexity of the techniques implemented, their degree of technicality, and their cost can only accelerate the marginalisation of small-scale farmers all over the world,' warns Arnaud Apoteker.[7] 'Every increase in the degree of complexity of agricultural practices, with the global liberalisation of exchange, has caused a phenomenon of concentration of agricultural production owing to which bigger and more modern farmers have absorbed smaller farms, sending millions of rural folk towards big cities.' The associations for international unity and environmental protection point out that 'This phenomenon of vast marginalisation was already seen at the beginning of the first Green Revolution in the 1960s and 1970s. Thousands of small-scale farmers had then been pushed out of the agricultural sector and forced to move to cities in search of jobs.

They still form the core of the miserable masses in Third World cities where they suffer from chronic malnutrition.'[8]

This unpleasant scenario was repeated in a number of countries, one of which was Algeria. 'The development options initiated by different governments favoured industrialising industries, which absorbed all the financial, technical and energy resources to the detriment of agriculture,' in the view of Nora Berrahmouni, Adviser for Sustainable Development at UNDP in Algeria.

> Arable fields were marginalised and abandoned. The introduction of high production varieties (especially in coastal areas) led to the gradual neglect of cultivars and local varieties which were remarkably sturdy and adaptable to their growing conditions. On the other hand, urbanisation and the rural exodus of young people toward cities affected the relations that they shared with their land and also their own biological material. There are, however, a few pockets like oases and mountains where the local inhabitants still maintain these links. Inherited over centuries, traditional practices are jealously safeguarded by farmers who care for their heritage and their land. But what will happen in future when GMOs start wooing them and they are subjected to the pressure of the biotechnology machinery?

This concentration wave did not spare industrialised countries. The intensification of agriculture drove populations from rural land in Europe, as British agriculturist Wilhelmina Vanbeuningen can testify:

> We settled down on a 20-acre farm in 1978. It was a medium-sized farm for that period. The fourteen field workers in turn fed fifty-five people with their wages. For their shopping and entertainment, there were two shops, two pubs, a smithy and a railway station. There was no school, though, as it had just closed down. Today, you need an hour to go to the city for shopping, as the only shop that still remains is too small. The smithy and the station have disappeared and a lot of families have migrated to cities. However, the 'old folk', having had enough of city life, are coming back to spend their retired lives in peace. But this has led to an imbalance in the age-group pyramid. Human 'biodiversity' has also changed.

The situation is little better in the US, according to Neil Ritchie.

For farmers in the US, the main difficulty has been trying to earn a fair income or wage in an economic system that is largely outside of their control.... Recently, prices for crops and livestock have been far below the cost of production. Farmers are going bankrupt in large numbers. The marketplace irony is that the lower prices for raw materials go, the more the farmers need to produce in order to make their debt payments. The more they produce the lower the prices go, and the spiral continues until the producer has no equity left and no cash to make payments. Producers use every shortcut available in an effort to squeeze out more production and good stewardship practices are often ignored. Many states in the United States are facing extreme pollution from large-scale animal feed lots. Fish found dead in our rivers and streams due to manure 'spills' are common, as are reports of toxic fumes making people ill and regions uninhabitable.... These chemicals are showing up in our wells, our rivers, and even in the Gulf of Mexico where nothing, apart from algae, can live. There have also been problems of crop failures that have affected significant portions of our wheat and cotton crops in the past few years. These blights thrive on monocultural fields and continue to plague producers because the biodiversity in seed stock has been dramatically reduced.

And the economic condition of American farmers is not going to improve with the use of GMOs. The ongoing technological progress, on the contrary, is constraining them even more financially. 'Proprietary seed technology and exclusive contracts for chemical application have driven up farmers' costs with no commensurate reduction in other production costs nor increases in market prices,' continues Ritchie. 'Despite record harvests, farmers are going out of business at a near record pace and small town economies are going with them.'

From farmer to producer of molecules

The situation of farmers in the very country which resorts most to GMOs certainly indicates what the future of farmers the world over will be if transgenic plant varieties are developed only with the idea of intensifying production. Choked financially by increasingly heavy costs, farmers may also have to face a lowering in the sale price of their harvest. By making a plant produce a molecule (a fatty acid, for example), that other plants produce naturally, transgenesis offers buyers the possibility of diversifying their supply sources and therefore strengthening their negotiating power. 'Cultivated plants as such are no longer the raw material; it is the products they contain that are important, products that different plants can be made to produce with the help of genetic engineering,' explains Arnaud Apoteker.[9]

> Users of raw materials, particularly the agro-food industry, can thus choose their supply sources according to the market rates, technological progress and political stability of the region. This will most probably result in the prices of raw materials coming down sharply and a weakening of the negotiating power of the producers. The economic victims of such a situation will be farmers as they will be reduced to mere producers of molecules as per the needs of the market.

The threat of a totally controlled agriculture, with farmers reduced to the rank of mere sowers of seeds developed in laboratories by multinationals, looms large. With transgenic plants, the freedom of agricultural practice and liberty of choice is reduced as the farmer works with a patented product which is subject to very specific conditions of use. For example, contracts for the use of a transgenic soya variety that is resistant to the herbicide RoundUp forbids, amongst other things, the cultivation of other varieties, the use of herbicides other than those allowed by Monsanto and the exchange of seeds with neighbours. Moreover, the farmer has to allow the company to conduct inspections on his fields for three years.

In addition, there is the inevitable disappearance of knowledge as farmers lose their traditional role as guardians of biodiversity and breeders–adapters of environmentally advantaged varieties. Nora Berrahmouni expresses her concern:

> The attachment of the farmer to this activity is all the stronger since his ties with his land and biological material are important. The value of the biological material depends on the quality of treatment that it

was subjected to for maintenance, preservation and selection of varieties/ecotypes. However, the efficiency of these treatments reflects the know-how of the farmer. His attachment to the land is closely linked to his production capacity and his mastery over biological material. Often names of regions were lent to various varieties cultivated by local farmers who, using their own breeding techniques on plants that they had reproduced over several decades, were able to encourage the assertion of particular genomes. Realising the importance of this three-dimensional and complementary system (man–land–genetic resources) is essential for future development of agriculture. The insertion of imported seeds or organisms in the production system may bring conjectural gains. However, this practice leads to the neglect of local biological resources and especially specific techniques of multiplication and enhancement which gave this system its autonomy. [There is] a break in the inter-generational transmission of messages, knowledge and techniques, pushing collective memory irretrievably into an abyss.

Ecological threats in countries of the South

Farmers in countries of the South have most to fear from this genetic revolution. At present they buy fewer seeds than their counterparts in the North, who are already practising intensive agriculture. Specialists estimate that in developing countries about 80 per cent of the seeds used come from farmers' fields, whereas in France, this proportion is about 50 per cent for all cereals and only 5 per cent for certain plants like maize where hybrid seeds have become widespread. The shock, therefore, can be much greater – all the more so because farmers in the South lack information on GMOs and easily fall prey to the retailers, as explained by Dominique Louette from the Manantlan Institute of Ecology and Conservation of Biodiversity (IMECBIO) of the University of Guadalajara (Mexico).

In Mexico, the technical support service for agriculture was dismantled several years back. Farmers therefore can only interact with the agricultural input retailers and representatives (very well organised) of seed manufacturers for business regarding their crops. They also represent the only professional outlets for the farmers. Besides which, if Mexican farmers are capable of using chemical products in conditions that are hazardous for their health, why should they not be open to 'big brother's' transgenic variety seeds when repeated clandestine visits have fostered their admiration for the USA's technical performance in agriculture?

There is also the grave danger of some Asian, African and South American countries hosting the experiments of seed makers who wish to circumvent the strict regulations of industrialised countries. 'Most often, it is the countries of the South that are used as cheap laboratories for developing transgenic plants as they have fewer regulations and this makes it easier for the producers to develop their crops faster in the off-season,' accuses Arnaud Apoteker. Peter Muchambo also expresses his fears:

> Poor countries have a tendency to favour creation of jobs or earning foreign currency to the detriment of soil or environment. Because of poverty, farmers are more easily lured into accepting the offers of multinationals who ask them to serve as 'guinea-pigs' and rent out their fields. When the experiment is over and their land is restored, it is unproductive and irreparably damaged by the chemical products that were used. Thus, the farmer has to rely on state aid for survival.

Unregulated experiments in certain countries have multiplied over the past few months. According to José Hermero Hoffmann, Secretary of State for Agriculture in the State of Rio Grande do Sul, Brazil, who chose to produce soya which is not genetically modified, 'more than 600 experiments with transgenic seeds are currently being conducted in Brazil, of which hardly 10 per cent are under the control of the federal Ministry of Agriculture' (as reported in *Le Monde*).[10]

Cocoa in wheat?

Another serious threat for developing countries is the probable loss of their traditional export products. As we have seen, new techniques of transgenesis make it possible to integrate a synthetic gene of a molecule into plant X, whereas it is naturally produced in plant Y.

'The consequences of this process on the economies of the South will be extremely serious when it becomes possible – very soon, according to some specialists – to produce cocoa, vanilla or palm oil in plants in the North or in greenhouses,' warns Arnaud Apoteker. Farmers in Africa and Asia will not be able to keep up with their European counterparts. This is underlined by Marc Dufumier, Professor at the Institut National d'Agronomie Paris Grignon and specialist in tropical agrarian systems, in an article published in 1998.[11] 'Farmers of the Third World whose tools are mostly manual or animal driven cannot compete with the highly mechanised production systems of farmers in industrialised countries. There are very few agricultural products for which such production technique differences do not exist between the North and the South.'

Since 1995, according to the Panos Institute, an NGO specialising in disseminating information on issues related to developing countries, American farmers have reaped their first harvest of rape seeds genetically modified to produce lauric acid, a raw material that is essential in the cosmetic and soap industries. Traditionally this acid is extracted from palm and coconut oils, 80 per cent of which are produced in Indonesia and the Philippines. The disappearance of this market – one of the most important in Filipino agriculture – would affect 30 per cent of the population. One need not go that far: the very existence of this new source of production would affect the prices. 'Given the conditions of productivity in major rape farms in the US, there is growing concern that farmers in the Philippines would be forced to sell their coconut oil at very low prices,' explains Marc Dufumier. Calgene, the company that is marketing genetically modified rape, states that this transgenic plant will not compete with palm and coconut oil but only help in compensating for the shortage when the production of tropical oil is low – a bit difficult to believe, as the temptation to increase its cultivation must be strong. Developing countries are likely to be the greatest losers in this genetic revolution.

Outcry about Biopiracy

The decision of the American Supreme Court in 1980 to authorise the patenting of living beings (see Chapter 7) marked the beginning of a race for patents which is playing havoc with the plant heritage of the countries of the South.

Biopiracy is a new way of exploiting the resources of local communities – not only the biological resources used traditionally in developing countries, but also their intellectual resources, their knowledge and know-how about the world of living beings. As well as food and medicinal plants, micro-organisms and animals, biopiracy targets the human genes of aboriginal communities which are of interest to science. Depending on the way it is practised (respect or non-respect for the rule of obtaining the informed consent of communities, partnership in the development of new products from genetic resources, sharing of profits, etc.), bioprospection can become a form of biopiracy.

Living species are seen as 'genetic resources', genes are seen as protein factories, the living being is reduced to the state of an industrial product protected by intellectual property rights: companies dealing in life sciences are jumping into what they call 'bioprospection' but the indigenous populations call 'bio-piracy'…. Scientists in multinationals are prospecting within indigenous populations for species which will be studied in laboratories in the North and patented there if useful genes are identified. In this way, the quinoa from the Andes and neem from India, which have been used traditionally for thousands of years, have today become the property of North American companies or institutions under the protection of a patent which could, if necessary, forbid local populations from cultivating them without paying royalties. Human cell lines from tribes in Panama and the Solomon Islands have also been extracted for medical study and patented in the USA (Arnaud Apoteker, Greenpeace France).

By allowing the isolation of the DNA segment(s) responsible for a particular trait in a plant or a bacterium, making it possible to insert them into the genome of another plant or animal and patent this new transgenic 'product', new biotechnology is only increasing this phenomenon of appropriation.

Other examples of biopiracy denounced by RAFI:[12]

- The University of Toledo (USA) holds two patents on an endod compound (soap) that was improved and cultivated by the women of Ethiopia. Ethiopian scientists have researched this compound extensively in order to control schistosomiasis, a widespread and devastating disease in Africa.

- More recently, the Australian company ForBio, in collaboration with the University of Hawaii, claimed property rights over a caffeine-free coffee plant whose genes of interest come from Réunion Island. The local population was aware of these characteristics for a very long time.

- Essential components of a medicinal plant in Madagascar, the periwinkle, were patented by an American pharmaceutical company that reaped hundreds of millions of dollars per year by selling medicines to treat cancer.

- At the beginning of this decade, Australian university scientists obtained a rare and drought-resistant bovine race from Zimbabwe. Today, the Tuli race is part of the tropical cattle herd of Australia and is being marketed in the US and Canada.

- A well-known and well-protected rice species which is used as food to tide people over periods of famine, and which is common in West African markets, was collected in Mali and sent for study to the International Rice Research Institute (IRRI) in the Philippines. Researchers at IRRI identified in this African rice a trait of resistance to a common disease and they allowed visiting scientists from the University of California (Davis) to patent this gene in the USA. As compensation for the African contribution, the university offered grants to scientists from West Africa. African farmers should also consider offering training to American scientists.

- The member states of the Organisation Africaine de la Propriété Intellectuelle (OAPI) also gifted brazzein, an ultra-sweet protein isolated from a berry plant in Gabon, where these qualities were well-known to the local populations. The University of Wisconsin received four patents on brazzein, from which production licences were granted to American biotechnology companies. They in turn are genetically engi- neering corn to produce this protein, because of the potential demand for sweeteners which is valued at US$1.4 billion at the world level. Gabon will not receive a penny. The OAPI will have the pleasure of learning that it has contributed to obesity in the US!

Notes

1 It should be noted, however, that Monsanto recently reinvented itself, and now wishes to be known as Pharmacia.
2 GRAIN and the Gaia Foundation, *World Trade and Biodiversity in Conflict*, Nos 1 and 2, available on the Internet site of GRAIN: www.grain.org.
3 Carine Pionetti, *Semences et savoirs en Inde, diversités en péril* (Culture Croisées Publi- cations, December 1998).
4 Appeal from Greenpeace, Confédération Paysanne, Solagral, Vétérinaires sans Fron- tières and other associations for international unity and environmental protection to denounce the presentation of GMOs as a solution to the problem of hunger, 1998.
5 Reported by Jean-Pierre Berlan, director of research at the National Institute for Agricultural Research (INRA, France) in *Le Monde*, October 1998.
6 Appeal from Greenpeace *et al.*, *op. cit.* 1998.
7 *Ibid.*
8 *Ibid.*
9 *Ibid.*
10 Reported by the French daily *Le Monde* on 26 May 1999.
11 Mark Dufumier, 'Securité alimentaire, commerce international et droits de l'Homme', Appeal from Greenpeace *et al.*, *op cit.* 1998.
12 *Small-scale Farmers Trapped in the Agreements on Trade Related Aspects of Intellectual Property Rights (TRIPS)*, RAFI, April 1999.

2

TERMINATOR, OUT!

Farmers' Autonomy Jeopardised by Sterile Seeds

'We should clearly say "No" to terminator technology and all related technologies that aim at preventing a seed from germinating when replanted.'

The latest technology for sterilising seeds has been dubbed 'Terminator'. No nickname could have been more appropriate for an invention that threatens to place farmers at the mercy of seed producers. While innovation directed at the needs of industry is nothing new in agriculture, genetic engineering at the service of an agro-industrial monopoly can make agriculture totally dependent. In March 1998 a patent was awarded to an American firm, Delta and Pine Land Company, and the United States Department of Agriculture for a biotechnology that makes it possible to prevent the germination of harvested seeds. It is a kind of biological lock, which is in the interests of seed traders, but is extremely worrying for small farmers. That's the reason RAFI has given it the nickname of 'Terminator Technology'. With Terminator, the agro-chemical giants have finally found a way of forcing farmers to buy new seeds each year, since the seeds that they harvest would be sterile. And these companies are the only ones who gain from this procedure. This new technology has nothing to offer to agriculture, other than new environmental and health risks. Indeed, it is such a disquieting prospect that the 'big bad sterilising gene' has managed to evoke almost unanimous opposition in just a few months. But this defensive mobilisation should not falter, for Terminator is just one of many applications of the technology that makes it possible to 'control the expression of genes'. The worst is undoubtedly yet to come.

Terminator: the sterilisation of living organisms

How does Terminator really work? While the basic principle is quite banal – a sterilising gene is introduced into a plant's genetic heritage so that it produces biologically sterile seeds – the implementation of the technology is far less simple. The process is somewhat difficult to understand but does merit some attention. It is disconcerting to see the wealth of ingenuity that has been exploited solely with the aim of sterilising living material. 'The technology depends on the insertion of three elements in the plant's DNA,' specifies Martha L. Crouch, who used the example of Terminator cotton to explain the way it works in an article published in 1998.[1] Gene A, which controls the synthesis of a toxin that stops the production of proteins, is inserted in the genotype of a plant. Gene A is activated by a promoter of gene B, which only intervenes late in the plant's development process. Hence, gene A, too, only becomes active later, which makes it possible to make the plant's seeds sterile without disturbing the normal growth of the plant. If gene A was activated right from the initial germination cycle, seed producers would never be able to produce seeds with a view to selling them, since the seeds would themselves be sterile. Hence, engineers insert a repressive fragment of DNA into the plant, between the gene B promoter and gene A. This fragment prevents gene A from becoming active, thereby making the seeds sterile. Once the seed producer has produced an adequate amount of non-sterile, sterility-bearing seeds, all he needs to do is remove from these seeds the repressive DNA fragment that blocks the process of sterilising the seeds that produce the plant. And nothing could be easier.

In fact, the DNA fragment disappears under the action of an enzyme called recombinase. The synthesis of this enzyme is itself controlled by a promoter that reacts to chemical treatment, in this case tetracycline. Just before selling the seeds to farmers, the seed producer therefore treats them with tetracycline, which engenders a chain reaction. The antibiotic triggers the promoter that controls the synthesis of the enzyme recombinase. This enzyme kills the DNA fragment that blocks the sterilisation gene promoter. Once the plant has grown sufficiently, the promoter releases this gene, which in turn controls the synthesis of the toxin that stops protein production. The result is a plant that reaches maturity normally, but bears sterile seeds.

This was the redoubtable invention developed and patented in 1998. Since then the multinational company Monsanto has tried to buy up the Delta and Pine Land Company and to negotiate with the

United States Department of Agriculture on the Terminator patent in
order to obtain exclusive rights over the technology. The other agro-
chemical industry giants are not to be outdone. Monsanto's four
major competitors – AstraZeneca, Novartis, Du Pont/Pioneer and
Aventis – have their own versions of Terminator technology, which,
depending on the firm, is called variously 'gene protection', 'genetic
use restriction' or 'gene expression control'. In the end, the objective
is the same – preventing harvested seeds from germinating in order to
force farmers to repurchase new seeds every year.

Nothing in it for farmers

With Terminator, seed producers have achieved their supreme goal –
enslaving their clients. As Jean-Pierre Berlan, research director at
L'Institut National de Recherche Agronomique (INRA), explains in
an article published in the French monthly *Le Monde Diplomatique*,[2]
'Terminator is only the starting point of a long process of confiscation
of living organisms, a process that began the moment that biological
heritage started to be treated as merchandise.' This has been a 'long
process' which began as early as the nineteenth century with the dete-
rioration technique, followed by hybrids in the 1930s – varieties that
already forced farmers to buy new seeds every year, since succeeding
generations produce far lower yields than first generation hybrid seeds.

> Hence, there's no difference between the 'deterioration' technique of
> the end of the nineteenth century, the technique of hybrids, and the
> Terminator technique. The only new development stems from the
> political context. Until recently, investors could not reveal their
> ambition – sterilising the living organism – without jeopardising it in
> the same breath. Farmers represented a powerful social category. The
> living organism was sacred. However, farmers are slowly dying out –
> they have been transformed into agriculturists, forever on the look-
> out for any kind of progress that could delay their inevitable elimina-
> tion. As far as living organisms are concerned, they have been
> reduced to a source of profits, mere DNA filaments. As for citizens,
> anaesthetised as they are by fifty years of neo-liberal propaganda, they

are conditioned to expect science and technology to provide solutions to the major political problems of our societies, whereas politicians are happy to limit themselves to management. Finally, small genetic breeding firms have given way to a powerful genetico-industrial complex with tentacles spreading as far as to the very core of public sector research. Terminator has simply shown us that this gigantic complex now feels strong enough not to have to hide its aim of confiscating living organisms.

Moreover, Terminator offers seed producers new market outlets. The sterilisation technology can be applied to crops not hybridised previously, such as wheat, rice, soya or cotton – which constitute an enormous market. Even in the case of varieties that can be hybridised, Terminator is a weapon that has proved even more effective than hybridisation in guaranteeing the repurchase of seeds. 'When Terminator is used, the second generation is killed. With hybridisation, the second generation is variable, but alive,' explains Martha L. Crouch.

And where do the farmers fit in all this? What has Terminator to offer them? The answer to these questions is as short as it is clear – nothing. 'A cash crop variety bearing this gene cannot be reproduced, thereby forcing farmers to repurchase the seeds each year,' explains IMECBIO's Dominique Louette of the University of Guadalajara (Mexico). 'This gene gives companies the means to guarantee the profitability of their investments and will offer no advantages to producers.' Indeed, seed producers themselves admit as much: 'Companies that are working in this field are sure that it offers many advantages, the first being that the investments necessary for developing these seeds are protected', Monsanto explained in one of its communiqués. In less diplomatic terms, Terminator's principal objective is to prevent farmers from keeping back or exchanging seeds, thereby forcing them to buy new ones every season.

It is undoubtedly true that this technology offers nothing but advantages to the multinationals. No longer will it be necessary to make farmers sign contracts in which they agree not to replant the seeds they harvest. Contractual sterility has been wiped out by biological sterility, which is far more effective, particularly in the countries of the

South where the lack of infrastructure sometimes makes legal pro-
ceedings difficult, but where the potential market is enormous. Indeed,
according to estimates, 80 per cent of the seeds used in the Third
World still come from the preceding harvest. Of course, farmers will
not be forced to buy these new, sterile seeds, but some NGOs fear that
they will receive strong incentives for doing so, which will only trap
them in a spiral of inflating costs, debts and dependence. In any case,
one can be sure that a company like Monsanto has its eye on these
new geographic outlets, as is proved by its submission of Terminator
patent applications in several developing countries.

A technology not devoid of risks

Above and beyond the ethical and economic issues involved,
Terminator is the bearer of several ecological and health risks, beginning with the contamination of neighbouring fields. According to
Dominique Louette, 'This gene, thrown into nature, can harm the
germinating capacity of contaminated seeds. It will therefore directly
harm traditional farmers whose system is based on re-using the seeds
of their local varieties every cycle.' As Martha L. Crouch confirms, 'It
is likely that Terminator will sterilise the seeds of neighbouring plants
of the same species, under certain conditions. However, these effects
would be confined to the first generation, and will not be able to
spread to other generations.' The explanation for all this is that the
pollen of Terminator plants bears the sterilising gene. This pollen,
carried by the wind or by insects to a neighbouring field where a non-
Terminator variety of the same crop is growing, can fertilise the crop.
The resulting seeds – first generation – will not be sterile, but their
seeds – second generation – could be sterile and are very likely to die,
although a few of the affected plants will survive.

   Contrary to the assertion of its promoters, Terminator is not the
absolute answer to genetic pollution due to the exchange of genes by
the spontaneous cross-breeding of transgenic plants with related wild
varieties (see Chapter 3). As Martha L. Crouch explains, 'Interestingly,
Terminator has been proposed as a method to prevent just such

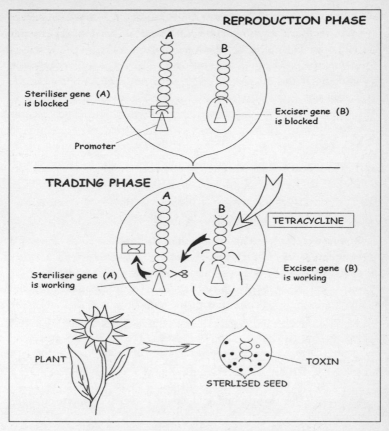

Figure 2.1 Seed terminator technology

escapes of GMOs and their genes. However, Terminator is not likely to function well for such purposes. First, it is unlikely that any tetracycline treatment will be 100 per cent effective. For various reasons, some seeds may not respond, or take up enough tetracycline to activate recombinase.' In this case, the plant's seeds will not be sterile. And its pollen, bearing a herbicide-resistant gene, may fertilise a plant of a variety that is quite close and transfer the resistance gene to future generations, which would not be sterile either. 'Another possibility,' Martha L. Crouch insists, is that even successfully activated Terminator genes may fail to make toxin because of a phenomenon called gene silencing. In experiments with other GMOs, it was discovered – quite unexpectedly – that in some cases, previously active (introduced) genes could suddenly stop working. If this phenomenon occurred with seeds containing the Terminator gene, plants containing the silenced toxin gene could grow and reproduce, perhaps for several generations. Thus, Terminator and other engineered genes could be carried into the future, to be expressed – perhaps still unexpectedly – at some later time.

To the fear of accidental contamination can be added the fear of the toxicity of seeds containing the toxin used to inhibit germination. 'In fact, the effects of the toxin on the uses of the seed are a serious question,' as Martha L. Crouch concludes:

> In forage crops, for example, not all of the forage is always harvested before seeds are mature, depending on conditions. How will a particular toxin affect birds, insects, fungi and bacteria that eat or infect the seeds? If a forage crop with toxin-laden seeds is left in the field, and the seeds come in contact with the soil, how will that affect the ecology of soil organisms? These are important questions because a variety of specific organisms are necessary for the healthy growth of plants. Further, a floral or ornamental crop with Terminator may happen to grow near a related crop where the seeds are used, and if pollination occurs, the seeds will contain toxin without the farmer knowing. The toxin could end up in products without anyone's knowledge.

Nor can we ignore the fact that we know nothing about the allergenic potential of this toxin for humans. We have the right to ask whether the treatment of seeds with tetracycline may enhance human resistance to antibiotics, which will turn into a serious public health problem (see Chapter 3).

No mercy for Terminator

For all these reasons, Terminator has managed to arouse suspicion all over the world. As Dominique Louette puts it, 'The development of this technology has made the strategy used by seed manufacturers very obvious. It has also, fortunately, aroused fear *vis-à-vis* GMOs, even amongst those who, until now, only foresaw its positive aspects.' According to RAFI, it has been almost unanimously condemned. The conference of the signatories of the Convention on Biological Diversity (CBD), held in Bratislava (Slovakia) in 1998, thus expressed its concerns *vis-à-vis* Terminator and asked governments to act cautiously. The CBD also set up a scientific group to study the technology. His recent speeches at the FAO make it obvious that the chairperson of this group has concluded that the Terminator technology is both dangerous and reprehensible. In October 1998, the Consultative Group on International Agricultural Research (CGIAR) – a network of experts appointed by the World Bank to manage a plant-breeding programme for underdeveloped countries – announced that it was not introducing Terminator technology into farmers' fields:

> The CGIAR will not include in its plant-breeding material any genetic system aimed at preventing the germination of seeds because of the potential risks of a sterilising gene flow through pollen, the non-viability of exchange or sale of seeds, the potential negative impact on genetic diversity and the importance of the breeding programme and reproduction on the farm for agricultural development.

This commendable consensus has already started bearing fruit. Patent holders are giving out reassuring signals. The AstraZeneca Company, the Wageningen University's Plant Biotechnology Centre (Netherlands) and the United States Ministry of Agriculture have all declared that they will not use Terminator. And on 4 October 1999 it was Robert Shapiro's turn to announce, as president of Monsanto, the radical reversal of position of his company. These initial signs are encouraging, but far from adequate. The public must remain alert lest the threat of this sterilising technology should surface again in a few years. It is necessary to continue to exert pressure on governments in order to compel them to refuse Terminator patents. International law grants them this power. In fact, the World Trade Organisation (WTO) provides for the rejection of an entire technology by virtue of its general regulations. Thus, Article 27.2 of the Agreement on Trade Related Aspects of Intellectual Property Rights (TRIPS, see Chapter 7) authorises states to 'exclude from patentability, any invention that might be perceived as detrimental to public order and morality if commercialised on their territory. This includes any threat to human, animal and plant safety or serious prejudice to the environment....' India has already announced that it will prohibit this technology for genetic sterilisation. The Brazilian State of Rio Grande do Sul and the state of New Hampshire in the USA are preparing to do the same. All the governments of the world should follow close on their heels.

Is the worst yet to come?

Terminator is just one aspect of a technology (called traitor technology by RAFI) that has far-reaching scope and is likely to further strengthen the dependence of farmers on a handful of multinationals. RAFI's Internet site reminds us that

> The brutish biological reality of this monopolistic strategy obscures the technology's more insidious dimensions. The two original Terminator patents – USDA/Monsanto (March 1998) and Astra Zeneca (September 1998) – actually prove that it is possible to switch on (or off) specific genes or, possibly, multi-gene traits by applying whatever external catalyst the company prefers. Although using the technology to create sterility is the most lucrative possibility, the same strategy could trigger other traits with other negative implications.... At one level, Traitor offers the opportunity to load a number of commercial characteristics onto a plant variety (or animal breed) which the company can choose to either activate or deactivate at or after the point of sale.... Farmers can buy seed like an industrialised farmer might buy a tractor – with or without the so-called 'value added' accessories. Depending on what traits the farmer can afford – or what traits the company wants to disclose – external chemical sprays or soaking could activate the purchased qualities in the platform seed.

Indeed, it's not by chance, according to RAFI, that patents connected with traitor technology all refer to a chemical catalyst. In the case of Monsanto's Terminator, it's the antibiotic tetracycline that makes it possible to activate the mechanism that leads to seed sterilisation. But for biotechnology firms, the ultimate goal is to reach a stage, very soon, where the trigger would be a product that they themselves manufacture. For, as everyone knows, life science specialists are also major chemical product manufacturers. This new technique gives them the means to increase their sales and win profits on all fronts – through both seeds and chemicals. 'Between March of 1997 and December of 1998, Novartis applied for no fewer than 12 closely related Terminator-type patents,' reports RAFI.

The patents explicitly propose that the suicide sequence within the seed could be triggered by herbicides or even fertilisers. More to the point, the patents note that the inducible promoted strategy proposed would have the effect of weakening the plant's natural resistance to pests and diseases. Novartis, of course, is in the business of manufacturing the chemicals necessary to compensate for the weaknesses it also manufactures. Farmers are sold addict seeds with junkie genes that will not perform well without chemical (or, for that matter, biological) supplements – including the purchase of augmented herbicides that trigger the seed's sterility. This is truly traitor technology.

And there's nothing exceptional about the Novartis case. Several other firms have submitted patents that allow them to go even further than the sterilisation of seeds. The final objective is to control properties other than sterility – 'positive' properties that would make it possible to improve the plant's quality characteristics and, on the other hand, 'negative' properties that would change them. But the basic principle remains the same – in the first case, a chemical spray makes it possible to activate these 'positive' genes, while in the second, it can deactivate 'negative' genes. And since the same firms manufacture and sell these synthesising inputs, there are profits all around. 'One might assume that the deliberate introduction of negative quality characteristics in seed would be a "hard sell" in the marketplace and among regulators. Not necessarily,' according to RAFI.

The original Terminator is itself a negative (or traitor) trait! RAFI is not theorising what the gene giants may do. In essence, they have already done it. There are more than two dozen patents – accepted and pending – that disclose variations on genetic sterility or traitor technology. If traitor technology is allowed to reach the market, industry will have won! It will have overcome the seemingly insurmountable hurdle of convincing regulators and farmers that using suicide seeds is acceptable in food production.

In other words, if we say 'Yes' to Terminator, other genes of the same type will follow. That's why Terminator should never step out of the laboratories.

The Apomixis Gene – an Underrated Risk

IMECBIO's Dominique Louette of the University of Guadalajara (Mexico) is concerned about the risks related to the Apomixis gene, which would, in her view, be as dangerous as Terminator for the genetic resources of corn.

Of the biotechnologies developed so far, the ones which, in my view, are the most likely to have a negative impact on the genetic resources of corn present *in situ*, are the Terminator gene and the Apomixis gene. The dangers related to the Terminator gene have been described several times already.... The risks related to Apomixis are not as widely known. Apomixis is a mode of reproduction of plants in which the plant produces grains without any fertilisation, like vegetative reproduction. It makes it possible to fix the genetic structure of a population, to a certain degree. An apomictic variety can be reproduced over several cycles with no noticeable changes in its characteristics. This technology, so far not very widely criticised, is even being defended by the same people who criticise GMOs. According to those who advocate it, Apomixis may be of interest both for hybrid varieties as well as traditional varieties. For commercial varieties, they maintain that an apomictic hybrid variety could be renewed through its seeds, collected during the harvest, without any noticeable decline in its hybrid strength, thereby making it unnecessary to change – and therefore repurchase the seeds for each new cycle. As for traditional varieties, they maintain that Apomixis will enable farmers to select seeds more effectively. In fact, the absence of genetic recombination will make it possible to ensure that the seeds selected from a good ear of corn would produce good ears of corn in the following cycle, like the mother plant, something that is difficult to ensure if the seeds result from fertilisation by pollen from another plant.

What is the real truth behind all the claims about Apomixis's advantages? The introduction of this gene in commercial varieties of species that reproduce naturally by cross-fertilisation – corn, for example – would indeed be economically interesting for farmers. Since the technology goes against the commercial interests of seed producers, however, it is not very likely that this gene will be introduced into commercial varieties one day. It will probably be used within these companies to fix the lineage, which will then cost far less to reproduce, in turn reducing the companies' seed production costs. As for the advantages of the presence of this gene in local varieties, there's nothing more uncertain. While the disadvantage of cross-fertilisation is that it leads to constant genetic recombination, thereby making it impossible to fix characteristics that are considered useful, the advantage is that it allows a large degree of plasticity, along with the capacity of species to adapt themselves over a period of time. Transforming a cross-fertilising species into an apomictic species would probably lead to a reduction in its capacity to adapt to changes in the environment. This characteristic is, perhaps, not very important for commercial varieties that are regularly replaced by new varieties. It is of fundamental importance, however, to traditional agriculture. Finally, introducing this kind of variety would risk changing the reproductive behaviour of local varieties and teosintes [the wild relative to corn], and therefore the very structure of their diversity. Who knows what the consequences of this situation could be on genetic resources of this kind? In the case of Mexico, we are dealing with what is, perhaps, the original source of corn. The profits of a few seed-producing companies and the country's wealthiest farmers should not weigh against the rights of small farmers and the diversity of a species that is as important to man as corn.

Notes

1 Martha L. Crouch, *How the Terminator Terminates, an Explanation for the Non-scientist of a Remarkable Patent for Killing Second-generation Seeds of Crop Plants* (1998). The author is Associate Professor of Biology at the University of Indiana (Bloomington, Indiana, USA) and can be consulted at RAFI's Internet site: www.rafi.ca
2 Jean-Pierre Berlan and Richard C. Lewontin, 'The Threat of the Genetico-industrial Complex' ('*La menace du complex génético-industriel*'), *Le Monde diplomatique*, December 1998.

3

THE PRECAUTIONARY PRINCIPLE
The Ecological and Health Risks at Stake

*'Considering the highly hazardous nature of GMO technology,
controlled by a few multinational companies, it is imperative to exercise
the greatest caution in trials and experiments involving GMOs.
The health rights of consumers should be adequately protected.'*

People react with fear to transgenic plants. This is testified to by the rejection of genetically modified organisms by farmers, citizens and consumers. And if GMOs are feared, it may be because transgenics appears to be a dangerous technology in the eyes of the public and even some members of the scientific community. They believe that these technologies are dangerous because they involve certain health risks, along with a number of ecological risks. Obviously, none of this has yet been proven – neither the hazardous nature of transgenic crops, nor their harmlessness. With the passing of time, however, more and more studies have confirmed initial doubts. People are naturally amazed that governments have allowed GMOs to be introduced into the food chain without first having obtained concrete guarantees of their harmlessness from biotechnology firms. Applying the precautionary principle in GMO trials and experiments has never been as urgent and important as it is now. Caution should become the order of the day.

Lack of adequate foresight

Caution is called for first of all because transgenics is a total departure from traditional methods of varietal breeding practised by farmers and seed producers. 'The production of transgenic crops does not simply constitute a further step in the process of improving the qualities of cultivated plants through procedures developed and practised by farmers since agriculture began, and by seed producers over the last few decades,' explains Greenpeace France's Arnaud Apoteker.

> Ever since humankind began to grow crops, the desire to improve the quality of the plants has never ceased. Farmers first used empirical methods by selecting the best plants and crossing them with other varieties of the same species; since the nineteenth century, more

sytematic methods have been adopted. Until the advent of genetic engineering, however, plant improvement methods did not upset 'the order of Nature', since the constraints of sexual reproduction and the notion of the species still reigned. Only varieties of the same species or of very closely related species were crossbred. Genetic engineering represents a radical qualitative leap, since it makes it possible to free the discipline from the 'species barrier'. Theoretically, it makes it possible to select useful genes from any living organism, whatever the kingdom it belongs to – virus, bacteria, plant, animal or human – and insert them into a plant. This is what makes it so fundamentally different from what was being done until now in the field of plant improvement. Genetic engineering makes it possible to create new living organisms by selecting parts from various other kingdoms of the living world and putting them together like so many Lego blocks. But by doing so, man is interfering directly in the very process of evolution. Indeed, ever since life began on Earth three or four billion years ago, evolution itself has moved towards the production of more and more complex beings, who became so dissociated over time that they could no longer be crossed sexually – in other words, they could no longer exchange their genes. This was the process of 'speciation' – the formation of species, one of the fundamental characteristics of evolution. By making the barriers between the species permeable, however, and creating new organisms hitherto unknown in nature – organisms with no evolutionary history and no natural predators, whose behaviour is unpredictable – transgenics constitutes a kind of reverse evolution.

This is an evolution whose ecological and health impacts are as yet unpredictable. Indeed, compared to the time frame of scientific knowledge, transgenics is still in its infancy, and even more so in the context of evolution's three or four billion years. In fact, only 50 years have gone by since Watson and Crick discovered DNA's double-helix structure (1953) and just thirty since we learnt to separate portions of DNA and insert them into another DNA with the help of restrictive enzymes (1970). After that, everything raced out of control. In 1973 came the first genetic engineering experiment on a bacterium, *E.Coli*. In 1982, the first transgenic animal was bred, a mouse. In 1983, the first transgenic plant was produced, tobacco. In 1994, marketing of these plants began with the launch of the Calgene company's slow-maturing tomato, withdrawn in 1997 owing to a lack of satisfactory results. Barely twenty years elapsed between the beginning of transgenics and the marketing of genetically engineered food products. That is very little time. 'The first transgenic plant was marketed in 1994, with no foresight as to any phenomena that could have considerable ecological, economical, social and ethical repercussions,' comments Arnaud Apoteker. 'It must also be noted that despite its eminently technical and complex character, transgenics today can be likened, in a sense, to tinkering around, since we don't really know exactly what we are doing, where exactly the gene is being inserted, what the unintentional effects may be, and so on.'

A commercial success

In a word, we don't really know all that much and we will have to wait a few years before we learn a little more. This is also the verdict reached by Dominique Louette:

> Genetically modified organisms are very recent inventions. Not enough time has passed for us to be able to foresee the actual effects of their use, without risks, both on the environment and on human health. The precautionary principle requires us to limit risks to the minimum, particularly those we are unable to control.

Apoteker speaks for his organisation:

> Greenpeace, an environment protection association, has focused specifically on the potential ecological consequences of the dissemination of genetically engineered organisms into the environment. It's clear that the consequences are largely unforeseeable and that the risks are truly incalculable in the light of the present state of knowledge. The lack of data on the long-term effects of the dissemination of GMOs is widely recognised by the scientific community.

Test crops cannot help us foresee with any certainty or exactness what would happen in cultivated fields, for the results of small-scale tests carried out in laboratory conditions cannot be extended to cover cash crops raised by farmers in complex ecosystems.

And yet, Apoteker reminds us, transgenic crops are being sold almost all over the world.

> Despite shortcomings in our knowledge concerning molecular genetics, despite the potential impact of the distribution of these engineered crops, in no other field do commercial applications follow so closely on the footsteps of scientific discoveries, which have become barometers of success for multinationals in the stock market.

In just a few years, GMOs have become an inescapable reality in the world of agriculture. In 1998, just four years after the first few marketing authorisations, almost 30 million hectares of transgenic varieties of cotton, soya, corn, tomatoes, potatoes and rape had been planted. In the United States, for example, 25 per cent of the cultivated area for corn, 35 per cent for soya and 50 per cent for cotton were sown with genetically modified, pesticide- and herbicide-resistant seeds. And that's only the beginning! Major agro-industrial groups estimate that the global market for transgenic crops will quadruple in size between the year 2000 and 2005, rising from 5 to 20 billion dollars. What is most amazing is that GMOs are being sold even though technical results have not always proved equal to the promises made by their inventors.

For example, according to the Panos Institute, Monsanto's Bollgard cotton – genetically modified to produce *Bt* (*Bacillus thuringiensis*) toxin – did not match expectations during its first year of use, 1996. The pesticide effect was reportedly not powerful enough to kill all pests throughout the season. The following year, it was the turn of RoundUp-resistant cotton to show some signs of weakness – 20 per cent of the capsules from the first harvest of this transgenic cotton variety were deformed or flowered too early. Was this proof of the fact that you cannot do what you like with all genes? Perhaps, counsels Bharat Dogra:

> We must question the way a terribly simplistic vision of science has been promoted – a vision according to which certain characteristics of a living organism can be transferred to another living organism simply

by transplanting a gene, ignoring the entire genetic context in which it is implanted and which cannot truly be reproduced in a different genetic context.

Gene flow – a major environmental risk

What about the risks involved? As far as the environment is concerned, the gravest risk stems from the natural flow of genes between cultivated transgenic crops and related wild plants. Apoteker explains that

> cultivated plants exchange their genes by spontaneous cross-breeding with related wild varieties, which are often weeds. Thus, there is a high risk of foreign genes from other species – even other kingdoms, whether animal or bacteria – that are introduced into cultivated plants, being transferred to wild varieties. The consequences can be severe – both for the environment and for biodiversity. A herbicide-resistant gene introduced into rape may be transferred to weeds that we would like to kill, making them invulnerable and, perhaps, even invasive. An insect-resistant gene may also be transferred to weeds, thereby promoting the spread of the gene in the environment and destroying other species, while also disturbing the ecological balance among pollen-gathering insects.

This phenomenon could prove particularly pernicious in developing countries that are far richer in biodiversity than industrialised countries where the standardisation of crops has reduced the number of species cultivated. Transgenic crops may come up against related varieties in Zimbabwe or India more easily than in the USA or France. In Mexico, for example, various species of teosinte (the wild relative to corn) often develop in association with local corn varieties in cropped fields. Since this foodgrain is a cross-fertilising variety, there is a very real risk of teosintes being contaminated by the genetically modified crop.

What is all this being done for? Not very much, apparently. Biotechnology firms affirm that herbicide-resistant plants will enable us to reduce the quantity of pesticides used. In fact, nothing is less certain. According to a report published on 19 May 1999 by the US Department of Agriculture, there is only a 1 per cent reduction in the quantity of pesticides that are used in transgenic cornfields as compared to the quantity used for genetically non-modified crop varieties.[1] A study recently carried out by The Pesticides Trust reached the same conclusions. For this NGO, which fights against the misuse of pesticides, the choice of resistant plants will affect the kind of pesticides that will be used, but not the quantities required. 'In the final analysis,' the report concludes 'the introduction of a herbicide-resistant soya variety stems more from competition between businesses for a greater share of the market, than agricultural sustainability.'[2] That is quite logical, particularly since the main GMO producers are also major producers of chemical inputs. For a company like Monsanto, which manufactures RoundUp, to sell a RoundUp-resistant seed is the safest way of getting farmers to buy its products rather than those of a competitor. Respect for the environment is a secondary consideration.

Increasingly resistant insects

Another major risk, engendered this time by the advent of seeds that are resistant to certain pests, is the emergence of insects that are just as resistant. 'The rapid development of insect-resistant transgenic crops is a sure recipe for the development of super insects that are resistant to the toxins they produce,' Apoteker assures us.

> In fact, these plants have been designed to produce and employ toxins against pests. However, unlike classical insecticides that are used (generally over-used) at specific moments, transgenic plants produce toxins continuously, thereby exposing insects to them on a constant basis. This cannot but help further promote insect resistance, already proven with most of the insecticides being used today. In the same way, the development of disease-resistant crops is only likely to lead to the development of new diseases.

The widespread use of certain toxins such as those of the *Bacillus thuringiensis* type presents a serious problem for organic farmers. This example, aired by the Union of Concerned Scientists (an American association), tells us a great deal about the way GMO crops compete with sustainable farming practices. A gene that is toxic for insects (insects that are harmful to crops, but also, sometimes, useful insects) has been identified in a soil bacterium – *Bacillus thuringiensis*. This gene has been transferred to several major crop varieties, including corn, cotton and potatoes, and has therefore been spread over hundreds of thousands of hectares. In insect populations, resistance intensifies from one generation to the next and destroys organic farmers who treat their crops traditionally, with natural *Bt* solutions. IATP's Neil Ritchie is quite perturbed by the risks the large-scale use of these toxins represent to organic farmers.

> The mass market introduction of natural pest control substances like *Bacillus thuringiensis* (used to control rootworm) into multiple varieties of crops, will shorten the useful life of that natural substance from decades to a few years, thus eliminating one of the main tools of organic and sustainable farmers. In our history, we have learnt one thing about battles with nature. Nature always wins! Bugs and weeds adapt and develop resistance or tolerance to every substance we put on them, sometimes with disastrous consequences.

Some scientists believe that this phenomenon has already begun. According to GRAIN, some studies carried out in the United States show that resistance to *Bt* toxin will undoubtedly be propagated far faster than Monsanto's experts maintain. Recent experiments have confirmed these fears.[3] Finally, other experts are concerned that the *Bt* type toxin may kill harmless insects, contrary to seed producers' assertions that it only destroys striped and pink stemborers. As early as 1998, research indicated that *Chrysopa* larvae, which are predators on stemborers, might suffer from the ingestion of a toxin produced by transgenic corn, an accusation strongly supported by new studies.[4]

Biodiversity in peril

How will this affect biodiversity? It will certainly suffer important setbacks, because the introduction of GMOs is synonymous with intensification, with monoculture, and therefore with the demise of local varieties. The Green Revolution scenario may well be repeated. Carine Pionetti, an ethnologist and the author of a survey on biodiversity in India,[5] explains,

> Through all the years of the Green Revolution, biodiversity was baffled in several ways. Firstly, the diversity of local cropping systems was partially swept away by the spread of monoculture. Then, the range of cultivated species shrank while rice and wheat gained ground both in irrigated farming and in rainfed systems.... Finally, the range of cultivated varieties within a single species has been declining since the sixties.

Amongst the risks which this strategy implies is the decreasing resistance to disease and pests, as Bharat Dogra recalls.[6]

> In India, a task force on rice breeding consisting of eminent experts who had met at the Central Rice Research Institute in Cuttack in February 1979 wrote in its report that 'most of the high yield varieties [of the Green Revolution] are derivatives of *T(N)* or *IR 8* and therefore have the dwarfing gene of dee-geo-woo-gen. This narrow genetic base has created alarming uniformity, causing vulnerability to diseases and pests. Most of the released varieties are not suitable for typical uplands and lowlands, which together constitute almost 75 per cent of the total rice area of the country.

Increased impact on agrarian systems in the South

Farmers are far from equal in the face of the diverse nature of ecological risks. According to Dominique Louette, farmers in developing countries are far more exposed to these risks than those living in the developed countries of the North.

> In the case of GMOs, applying the precautionary principle would mean placing restrictions on the uncontrolled release into the environment of genes that could, for example, modify the genetic structure and behaviour of their wild relatives or of local varieties (through the emergence of 'superweeds', through changes in their modes of reproduction, etc.). Where restrictive measures cannot be

enforced, it should at least be possible to control the situation if a gene proves harmful to the environment. Farmers from developed countries and those from developing countries are not at par on this issue. In this context, the comparison between corn cultivation methods in the United States and the traditional Mexican system is very telling. In the US corn belt, farmers sow corn varieties in several dozen or several hundred hectares, while the size of plots in which traditional Mexican communities like Cuzalpa (Jalisco) sow just one variety rarely exceeds two hectares. On the other hand, in the USA, all the crop seeds are replaced every year, either because they are hybrid varieties that soon lose their hybrid strength over succeeding generations or because of contracts signed with seed producers who 'prohibit' the recycling of seeds. In Mexico, however, 60 per cent of the corn area is sown with local varieties and the seeds are collected from the preceding year's harvest. Finally, in Mexico, there is a high degree of trade in seeds between farmers within a community and between different communities. In fact, in the community that was the subject of the study, almost half the batches of seeds sown were seeds that had been procured from other farmers. A large number of varieties are introduced for testing each year (20 varieties introduced as compared to six local varieties). The seeds of a particular variety can therefore be transported over great distances from cycle to cycle.

How do these differences imply divergent risks in the two agricultural systems? Owing to the difference in the size of plots, a variety that is grown in Cuzalpa is far more vulnerable to genetic contamination by varieties growing in the plots around it than a variety grown in the American corn belt. The collection of seeds from the centre of an American plot of land is, so to speak, free of any external gene flows, while the probability of gene flows is far stronger for all plants growing in a plot in Cuzalpa. Sowing a genetically modified variety in this system therefore means that the gene(s) will certainly spread to the surrounding plots. On the other hand, due to the replacement of seeds in USA, the genes transferred by gene flow are not transferred to the following generations, while this does happen in Mexico, through local varieties or teosinte populations that develop in or around cornfields. Hence, if there was a gene that was found to be agronomically dangerous or hazardous for the survival of the varieties, the process could probably be halted quite rapidly and effectively in the USA by withdrawing the seeds containing the harmful gene from the market and sowing new varieties in the following cycle, since no local variety or wild relative would have been present and able to store the new gene and continue to spread it during succeeding cycles (although the same does not hold true for genes linked to other organisms – building resistance in insects, the modification of micro-organisms, etc.). In Mexico, however, a gene that is introduced in a variety that is being sown is a gene that has been 'hurled into nature' – it is not possible to stop it from spreading. Even if farmers who use transgenic varieties were to agree to play the game by refraining from using the same seeds or distributing them, the risk stemming from the mode of functioning of traditional cropping systems would still endure.

And what is true for Mexico is equally true for many other developing countries with similar agricultural systems.

The dangers for humankind

Health risks come next in the list of ecological risks. For although some of these risks are not entirely supported by scientific evidence, suspicion is already strong enough for the British medical weekly, *The Lancet*, to condemn the irresponsibility of the authorities and of biotechnology firms in a virulent editorial:[7] 'The policy [of the US Food and Drug Administration] is that genetically modified crops will receive the same consideration for potential health risks as any other new crop plant. This stance is taken despite good reasons to believe that specific risks may exist.'

Toxicity

The toxicity of some GMOs is the first issue. 'Genetic engineering can induce unexpected changes in the metabolic processes of genetically engineered organisms and cause the synthesis of new proteins or new components that may be toxic,' says Arnaud Apoteker.[8]

In fact, gene transfer techniques as they stand today do not allow us to direct the insertion of the foreign gene to a specific position in the genome. But the impact of the inserted gene depends on the spatial context within the receiving organism. The gene may cause phenomena that differ from the ones one may expect from the simple addition of isolated elements. The possibility of the development of such phenomena cannot be excluded when we introduce foreign genes into our food. Possible toxic products, resulting from unexpected changes following a transgenic intervention, cannot always be identified in food items. Analyses cannot help us find and measure the phenomena we are looking for – in fact, by definition, such unexpected effects may only be found once they reveal themselves.

Moreover, the recent findings of a British researcher according to which transgenic potatoes have harmful repercussions on the intestinal system of laboratory rats[9] will certainly not allay fears.

Allergic reactions

Second, scientists are concerned about the possibility of an outbreak of allergies in the future. Arnaud Apoteker warns that

the development or aggravation of allergies is one of the most obvious risks of consuming transgenic foods. In fact, allergies are caused by proteins, often the ones that play the role of protecting crops against pests and diseases. Yet insect resistance is one of the characteristics most often introduced into genetically engineered crops. Food products from genetically engineered plants often contain proteins that result from the action of a gene that has been introduced or modified, which may induce new health hazards. New proteins of viral, bacterial, plant and animal origin that genetic engineers are preparing to introduce into food crops have often never been part of the food we eat. Hence, their allergenic potential is completely unknown.[10]

Resistance to antibiotics

The most disquieting risk stems from the possibility of the development of resistance to antibiotics, which some GMOs may help enhance. As Arnaud Apoteker explains,

Several genetically modified crops contain antibiotic-resistant genes. Take Novartis's genetically modified corn, for example. These genes, which promote resistance to antibiotics, are not really of any use to the plant. They were inserted along with the target gene and helped in identifying cells that integrated the new gene. They are called marker genes. Afterwards, these totally useless genes are transferred to the succeeding generations and remain a part of the genetic heritage of the species and of all future varieties stemming from it. It is possible, however, to remove these antibiotic-resistant genes. From the point of view of health concerns, it is quite disturbing to note that genes that are resistant to antibiotics that are commonly used for human and animal health are being spread into the environment.[11]

These marker genes could easily be transferred to certain bacteria. This is a frightening thought, since we already know that the number of antibiotic-resistant pathogenic bacteria is on the rise. Indeed, the European Union's Scientific Management Committee has itself recently sounded the alarm.[12]

New viruses

Finally, the advent of virus-resistant transgenic crops is just as alarming a prospect, since it may lead to the development of viruses that do not exist in the natural environment. In fact, genetically modified plants may even exchange their viruses with other infected viruses, thereby generating new and totally unknown viruses. According to the Panos Institute, scientists from Agriculture Canada have demonstrated this possibility.[13] They developed a virus strain lacking the gene for a specific protein needed to infect new plant cells. They then took an equivalent gene from another virus and inserted it into the host plant's DNA. In plants artificially infected with the disabled virus, new and fully infectious viruses appeared within ten days.

A plea for the precautionary principle

All these health and ecological arguments speak in favour of the application of the precautionary principle. Some governments – such as

Norway, Austria and Luxembourg – have already invoked this caution
in refusing to accept Novartis's *Bt* corn crops in their territory. They
have banned these crops for two reasons: the harmful effects on biodiversity of the *Bt* insecticide gene and the harmful effects of the
antibiotic-resistant gene which this variety also contains. According to
Greenpeace, the Norwegian government has declared as much in the
summary of its paper banning the variety, maintaining that

> [Novartis' *Bt* corn] cannot be considered a significant positive contri-
> bution, either for society at large or for sustainable development.
> Ethically speaking, this product offers no demonstrable benefits that
> would counterbalance the health risks it presents. Consequently, the
> sale of this product would be against the precautionary principle.[14]

The signing in January 2000 of a Biosafety Protocol regulating
trade in GMOs embodies the international recognition of the precautionary principle. The final text clearly recognises the right of
any country to refuse the import of transgenic seeds even if there
is no available evidence of their harmfulness to human health or to
the environment:

> The lack of scientific certainty linked to insufficient information and
> relevant scientific knowledge ... cannot withhold [a country] from
> making a decision on the import of GMOs with a view to avoiding or
> reducing to a minimum their potential adverse impact.

This provision only applies to living material (such as transgenic seeds
or modified bacteria). Processed products which are dead and can no
longer spread in the environment will not be liable to embargo at
borders. The Protocol also creates a space for states to 'take into
account the socio-economic factors' of the impact of GMOs when
making a decision. The Montreal agreement is a first victory for those
in favour of a cautionary approach to GMOs. The next step is to
ensure that governments actually enforce the precautionary principle
as often as necessary.

In fact, this principle does not imply rejecting the entire gamut of
GMOs, but examining each case and identifying dark areas. In short,
it is a principle of prudence and moderation that is entirely justified,

according to Dominique Louette, particularly in the present state of knowledge and in the present context.

The precautionary principle does not aim at damning all GMOs or saying, like the Mexican farmer who spoke of genetic enhancement, that 'Nature must be really upset to learn that we are trying to induce a plant to produce far more that She herself could make it produce.' There is no question of condemning all GMOs out of hand, since they differ in their objectives, in the procedures used to develop them, in their degree of complexity, and in the impact they may have. What is important is that we do not allow ourselves to be carried away by the craze for every new thing, every new technology, and that we do not allow ourselves to be taken in by arguments that are often not much more than mere commercials. What is important is that we adopt a critical approach, a 'healthy' fear, the kind that helps one imagine the worst in order to prevent it from happening. All the more when it comes to assessing a new scientific product, the primary motivation behind which is not one of saving the planet from hunger (or else we would have let ourselves be carried away ages ago), but rather of (the companies') profits and (the scientists') glory. It's a fear that many feel is unjustified. We can only hope that they are right. We must doubt the ethics of multinational plant-protecting and seed-producing firms, however, when insecticides or herbicides banned in their own countries are sold in the Third World. DDT, for example, is used to fight malaria in Mexican homes and their surrounding areas, even though this substance is popularly known as 'the one that kills the cats'. We must doubt their ethics all the more because, unlike the case with pesticides, proof of their negative impact has yet to be formally collected. What is most important is that we do not allow anyone to do just anything they like without question, such as distributing *Bt* varieties with short lifespans due to the monogenic resistance systems used so far, although they harm organic farming; or producing apomicitic varieties, which may well modify the reproductive system of the species and thereby reduce the adaptive capacity of local varieties – and which, combined with Terminator technology, will give the *coup de grâce* to local varieties and genetic resources (indeed, to an entire productive socio-economic system).

Notes

1 Reported in the French weekly *L'Express*, 17 June 1999.

2 Pesticides Trust, *The Price of Resistance* (November 1996), quoted in *Greed or Need? Genetically Modified Crops*, Panos Media Briefing No. 30A (February 1999).

3 According to a study by William McGaughey and his American colleagues at the University of Kansas, published in *Science*, 7 May 1999, some stemborer descendants may resist the ingestion of *Bt* type toxins, a toxin integrated in genetically modified corn strains to protect the crop from these pests. These descendants contain a partially dominant gene, which means that once one of the parents contains the gene, the resistance is transferred to the following generation. Until now, however, seed producers believed that the two stemborer parents both had to contain the resistance gene for their descendants to have it too. Hence, they used to advocate sowing non-transgenic corn plots next to *Bt* corn plots to enable the survival of stemborers that did not contain the gene for resistance. They believed that cross-breeding between the latter and stemborers that did contain the gene for resistance would lead to non-resistant descendants. According to researchers, however, if the phenomenon takes place in the field, the so-called high dose/refuge strategy could well prove unsuitable, since if just one parent had the resistance gene, it would be transferred.

4 A study by John Losey, Linda Rayor and Maureen Carter of Cornell University, published in *Nature*, 20 May 1999, shows that the pollen of the N4640-*Bt* variety's transgenic corn could be toxic for Monarch butterfly larvae (this is an American migrant butterfly). Of the larvae that had fed on corn sow thistle leaves sprinkled with *Bt* corn pollen, 44 per cent died in four days, while not even one of those that had fed on leaves sprinkled with non-transgenic corn pollen died. Although Professor Losey warned that 'Our study was carried out in the laboratory, and it would be out of place to draw conclusions about the risk for populations in the natural environment solely on the basis of these preliminary results', the publication of these findings pushed the European Commission to suspend all authorisations for transgenic corn. A spokesperson for the Commission said: 'The American findings will be submitted to the Scientific Committee and perhaps the Consumer Protection Committee as well. Although, *a priori*, there may be no immediate risks, we are bound to apply the precautionary principle.' On the other hand, no decision has been taken about the two Monsanto and Novartis species that have already been authorised.

5 Carine Pionetti, *Semences et savoirs en Inde, diversités en péril* (Editions Cultures Croisées, December 1998).

6 Bharat Dogra, *Our Fields, Our Seeds; Farmers' Self-reliance and Protection of Land Will Help Struggle against Hunger* (New Delhi, 1998, published by the author: address and contact numbers given in Appendix 3).

7 *The Lancet*, Vol. 353, No. 9167 (29 May 1999).

8 Arnaud Apoteker, 'Les dangers du génie génétique', article published in the dossier accompanying the appeal by Greenpeace, Confédération Paysanne, Solagral,

Vétérinaires sans Frontières and several international solidarity and environment protection associations condemning the presentation of GMOs as the solution to the problem of hunger, 1998.

9 Arpad Pusztai, a researcher at the Rowette Research Institute (UK), fed two groups of rats two different kinds of potatoes. The first kind were genetically modified to produce lectins, a family of insecticidal proteins found in some bean varieties. The second were enriched with lectins. The findings were as follows: some of the internal organs of the rats fed on transgenic potatoes, including the liver, atrophied. Following these revelations about the potential harm of transgenic foods, Dr Pusztai, a well-known and experienced scientist, was subjected to very strong pressures by his Institute and forced to resign. Complete information about Dr Pusztai's position is available at the following website:
http://www.milleniumdebate.org/

10 Apoteker, 'Les dangers du génie génétique'.

11 Ibid.

12 In a report submitted to the European Commission in May 1999, the Scientific Management Committee called for curbs on 'the inappropriate use of antibiotics. The Committee has learnt that due to excess consumption, bacteria are becoming more and more resistant to antibiotics, with all the obvious disadvantages that ensue, particularly as far as the treatment of infectious diseases like pneumonia or tuberculosis is concerned.' The Committee has also trained its sights on, among other practices, the use of antibiotic-resistant marker genes that are introduced into GMOs.

13 Greed or Need? Genetically Modified Crops, Panos Media Briefing No. 30A (February 1999).

14 Greenpeace, information file on the Biosafety Protocol, January 1999.

4

GREATER TRANSPARENCY
The Politics of GMO Secrecy

'We note with concern that much work relating to GMOs has been shrouded in secrecy and misinformation. We call for complete transparency on the part of governments as well as corporations on all issues concerning GMOs. Considering the high hazard potential of GMOs, accountability for the risks associated with GMOs should be clearly established.'

Do biotechnology companies operate with transparency? Not really. Let us rather say that they only reveal what suits them best. In order to counter growing public distrust and to provide their race for profits with a humanitarian alibi, they launch massive publicity drives pledging that biotechnology is the solution to the problem of world hunger. Most other issues fall under the rule of silence. On the risks involved, mum's the word. What is even more serious, multinationals and governments seem to be refusing citizens access to the full information that would allow them to understand one of the most important questions in our society today. Whether the issue is one of labelling or experimentation in crop cultivation, this seems to be the age of obscurantism. The lack of transparency is equally in evidence when it comes to fixing the responsibility with regard to possible harm to the environment and to health. Who would pay the damages, in case of any problems?

A false solution to the problem of hunger

Biotechnology companies keep us totally in the dark, beginning with their actual objective, a frantic race for profits and patents. They would have us believe, however, that their only goal is to save the entire Earth.

> Today, we are unfortunately aware of the fact that sending food to underprivileged countries is not enough to solve the problem of malnutrition in the world. The only sustainable solution is to give each and every country the means of taking on the responsibility themselves in order to produce more food, and better food, to feed their people. In this respect, biotechnology offers real solutions.

For Monsanto, who posted this notion in advertisements published in the French press in 1998, there is no room for doubt – GMOs will help in alleviating the problem of hunger in the world. Neil Ritchie of the IATP was more sceptical:

> So-called 'life sciences' companies like the US-based agrochemical giants Monsanto and DuPont, with help from the US government, have been explaining their promotion of GMOs, agricultural indus-trialisation and near monopoly market concentration as necessary in order to 'feed the world'. From this platform, they have launched an incredible economic and public relations assault on farmers and consumers, both here in the US and around the world.

How do they plan to 'feed the world'? Nothing could be simpler, according to Robert Horsch, Director of Technology at Monsanto, who explained in detail the virtuous cycle of GMOs in a speech delivered at the end of 1997 in Austria.[1]

> The key contributions of biotechnology will be several-fold: producing more food on the same area of land, thereby reducing pressure to expand into wilderness, rainforests or marginal lands which support biodiversity and vital ecosystem services; reducing post-harvest loss of food (caused by disease, pests and decay) and improving the quality of fresh and processed foods, thus boosting the 'realised nutritional yield' per acre; displacing resource- and energy-intensive inputs, such as fuel, fertilisers or pesticides, thus reducing unintended impacts on environment and freeing those resources to be used for other purposes or to be conserved for the future; encouraging reduction of environ-mentally damaging agricultural practices and adopting more sustain-able practices such as conservation tillage, precision agriculture and integrated crop management; stimulation of a new kind of economic growth: more benefit with less input and harm.

Enticing, isn't it? The only problem is that this politically correct sales pitch does not stand up once we examine the facts. First, because the transgenic varieties being marketed today were designed to meet the agricultural needs of developed, and not developing, countries. In 1998, according to RAFI, 71 per cent of transgenic plants contained a herbicide-resistant gene, which is far from being a priority for farmers in countries of the South – and that's proof enough. 'Transgenic varieties have not been designed for small farmers, but rather to meet the objectives and modes of production of farmers in developed countries and affluent producers in developing countries,' explains Dominique Louette. 'These varieties are being produced with the so-called 'modern' agriculture system in mind, and do not take the constraints of traditional farming methods into account (marginal areas, low use of outside inputs, etc.). It is well known that in agriculture, producing what the poor eat is certainly not the road to prosperity – which is the motivating factor in the strategy adopted by seed firms.' It is no coincidence that most GMOs marketed by multinationals are for large-scale cash crops (corn, soya, etc.) that can be exported or used for cattle feed, and not food crops that are the staple diet of farmers.

Of course, research on the development of GMOs that are more adapted to the needs of developing countries – those resistant to salinity and drought rather than to herbicides or pesticides – is beginning. But the results are far from conclusive. For instance, salt's metabolism depends on the interaction of several genes. The greater the number of genes involved, the more difficult it is to predict the outcome of transgenics. And even if these seeds do become truly productive one day, whether the world's poorest farmers will be able to afford them remains to be seen. Dominique Louette again:

> Even if some seed companies express their willingness to work for small farmers – for instance, research being carried out by CINVESTAV[2] (Mexico) on the resistance of potatoes to two viruses – it is evident that the cost of these varieties (cost of necessary seeds and inputs for producing them, etc.) will be prohibitive for the farmers concerned, just as in the case of varieties that have been improved by conventional methods.

Sustainable development or a second Green Revolution?

In fact, all that the biotechnology companies are offering is crop intensification, reusing the 'good old recipes' of the Green Revolution and revising them, twenty-first-century GMO style.

And this is exactly where the problem lies. For this is not the way we can solve the problem of hunger in the world. Arnaud Apoteker:

> The Green Revolution experience has taught us that no technical revolution can lead us to victory over malnutrition. On the contrary, the complexity of the techniques developed, their highly technical nature and high costs can only further marginalise the world's small farmers …. The ecological impact of these monocultures, based on fertilisers, pesticides, irrigation and mechanisation, is considerable and constitutes a threat to food security. Transgenic crops are developed on the basis of the Green Revolution's high-yield varieties and may further worsen the food security problem due to an even greater degree of technicality, an increase in the quantity of herbicides used and a greater concentration of seed and chemical suppliers.[3]

The strategy of the struggle against the problem of hunger should, on the contrary, fit in with the logic of sustainable development. Researchers, farmers and NGOs throughout the world are developing different farming models that are not dependent on imported and costly technologies but on local expertise. For all these practitioners, the eradication of hunger and poverty depends on the implementation of several other measures as well, ranging from the cancellation of the debt of developing countries to the redistribution of land, and including the adoption of techniques that are adapted to the situation and do not harm the environment. The success of projects such as the one undertaken by Nepal's Jajarkot Permaculture Programme (JPP) has shown that this 'other' method of 'working with the soil' is not just a distant dream. The JPP advanced bit by bit, over six years, to cover more than fifty villages in four districts today. Its 12,000 members receive advice from this NGO, whose objective is to promote sustainable agriculture in accordance with the permaculture principles that its Australian inventor, Bill Mollison, defines as follows: 'The creation and upkeep of a productive agricultural ecosystem with the diversity, stability and resistance of a natural ecosystem.' Permaculture excludes any recourse to chemical inputs for increasing yields, preferring

natural fertilisers. 'A farmer in Gumi [one of the areas covered by the
JPP] has introduced sorghum as green manure, ploughed in after a
month's growth, prior to planting potatoes,' explains Chris Evans, a
JPP Technical Adviser.[4] 'He claimed a 300 per cent increase in potato
yield compared to the non-use of sorghum.' This is just one of several
examples showing that permaculture or other agricultural methods
based on principles other than the trio of fertilisers, pesticides and
high-yield seeds can lead to astonishing results.

'Only development options that advocate the rational use of land
and the development of land properties and local genetic resources
will enable the kind of productivity and sustainability that would
preclude both the need for and the use of GMOs,' is the view of Nora
Berrahmouni of the United Nations Development Programme in
Algeria, one fully shared by Dominique Louette:

> In Mexico, as elsewhere in developing countries, agricultural produc-
> tion levels are not limited, let alone to a large extent, by the genetic
> material of cultivated plants. These levels depend, above all, on the
> proper functioning of agrosystems. In various communities in the
> West of Mexico, the use of a small amount of phosphate-enriched fer-
> tilisers while sowing, the construction of stone barriers around the
> contour lines to reduce erosion, or direct sowing make it possible to
> curtail costs and/or increase corn yield by 20 to 50 per cent. What
> improved or genetically modified variety can yield such results?
> Believing that GMOs will solve the problem of world food produc-
> tion is tantamount to moving further down the same path that
> agriculture has followed for the last several decades, which has been
> vehemently disputed both from the environmental as well as the pro-
> ductive point of view. It means continuing to consider soil as just a
> support for the plants to anchor themselves, and pests and weeds as
> enemies that must be destroyed. It also means replicating the Green
> Revolution process by promoting technologies aimed at the most
> prosperous farmers.

Intensifying production at the cost of biodiversity

Following this path is all the more dangerous since crop intensification is necessarily accompanied by the decline of biodiversity, as the much-vaunted Green Revolution showed (see Chapter 3). High-yielding varieties replace crop varieties that are undoubtedly old, but much better adapted to local conditions. The deceptive advantages of intensive cropping patterns conceal the decline of the biodiversity maintained by farmers as an asset towards food security. That is enough to jeopardise rather than consolidate the food balance in a region. Arnaud Apoteker:

> Long-term food security is not based on agricultural intensification at all costs, but rather on biological diversity. Studies have shown that diversified ecological communities are more resistant to drought or other ecological imbalances that cause variations in populations of individual species. The same principles of diversity and stability are also used in conventional agricultural systems. A profusion of local varieties and stocks are cultivated for better adaptation to local ecological conditions and a greater range of resistance to different diseases and parasites.

While these diversification practices no longer exist in industrialised countries, they are still very much alive in countries of the South like India. Carine Pionetti's study shows that

> Traditional farming currently being practised in India with the overall objective of self-sufficiency is based on biological diversity. Crop diversification allows small farmers to be able to meet a large number of needs. Variation in crops is the key not only to nutritional balance but also to a certain stability in soil fertility and humidity levels. Moreover, this practice constitutes an effective method of pest control. In a system called *baranaja*, or 'twelve seeds', which is traditionally practised in the Garhwal region of the Himalayas, the seeds of a host of plants (millet, amaranth, sorghum, beans, soybean, green-gram) are sown together in order to optimise interaction in terms of height, root systems, moisture retention capacity and nutrient cycle. Although production levels are generally low in traditional farming,

these low-input systems ensure stable yields and have the advantage of
exhausting neither the resources nor the capacity of people to ensure
their own survival.[5]

And it is precisely the traditional farming model and the food security
it ensures that the intrusion of GMOs is likely to call into question.

However much agro-chemical multinationals may present themselves as universal saviours, the reality in developing countries has
shown that transgenic plants are more of a threat than an opportunity.
'Clearly, these efforts are not really about feeding the world,' is how
Neil Ritchie sums it up. In any case, he considers the problem of
hunger to be an outcome of poverty rather than food deficiency.
'According to Peter Rosset, Executive Director of Food First and co-
author of *World Hunger: Twelve Myths*, the world produces enough
food to provide at least 4.3 pounds of food per person per day. Hunger
is not a matter of inadequate production, but rather one of access and
distribution.' Indeed, this is a point of view that is shared by several
experts in the matter. Bharat Dogra concludes that

> The struggle against hunger and malnutrition demands action on
> several fronts – for land reforms and other steps which will bring
> equality, for conservation of water and protection of forests, for
> organic farming based on indigenous seeds and for opposing patents,
> GMOs and other recent onslaughts of big agribusiness interests.[6]

Lack of transparency

The fallacious discourses on food security by biotechnology companies are invariably accompanied by a lack of transparency on the
research they conduct. 'The misinformation, lack of clarity and
secretive nature of the work on GMOs internationally is a major
problem,' notes RAFI's Edward Hammond. For instance, it is difficult
to learn about the plots of land where transgenic plants are being cultivated. A study conducted in France by two associations, *Les Amis de la
Terre* (Friends of the Earth) and *France Nature Environnement*, highlighted the lack of transparency surrounding such trials – as many as

half of the 96 French Departmental administrations questioned refused to give any information concerning the sites where experiments on GMOs were being conducted. In India, too, farmers' organisations are coming up against the lack of clarity on the part of seed producers. 'A violent debate took place in Karnataka and Andhra Pradesh against Monsanto, which had introduced the cultivation of transgenic plants in test fields,' recounts Bharat Dogra.

> Farmers' organisations alleged that these tests were making use of Terminator technology. Monsanto's spokesperson replied that the technology in question was not being used there and that, on the contrary, these tests were using GMOs that would help reduce the use of chemical pesticides. Certain activists then retorted that on no account should a company that owns the patent for the Terminator technology be authorised to conduct tests in Indian fields.

A similar lack of transparency also surrounds the incorporation of GMO products in various foods. Europe is pretty well the only region where appropriate measures were taken to inform consumers.[7] On 11 January 2000 the European Commission adopted the proposal made by the Standing Committee on Foodstuffs to render compulsory the labelling of products containing ingredients which, taken individually, contain over 1 per cent of transgenic material. This regulation will also apply to flavourings and additives, unlike the previous law adopted in 1998. European buyers can thus freely choose food products devoid of GMO. In other parts of the world, however, transparency is still not translated into law. And it may well not be for quite some time.

Indeed, the Biosafety Protocol adopted in January 2000 by over 130 countries to regulate the global trade in GMOs fails to address the issue of labelling. The main exporting countries (US, Canada, Argentina and Australia) have categorically rejected the demand made by the European Union to label every GMO product. The only obligation will be to indicate whether a shipment 'may contain GMOs', without any additional detail on the nature of the GMO product. The Protocol does call for a new round of negotiations on a separate labelling for GMOs which are to be concluded two years at the most after the present treaty comes into force. But the intervening period before the ratification (a minimum of two years) will delay this obligation to label by at least four years.

In short, the time when the consumer will be able to exercise a preference for guaranteed GMO-less products is yet to come. Arnaud Apoteker:

> The intentional combination of transgenic and conventional products means that it is impossible for consumers to choose products that are exempt from genetic contamination. Food product manufacturers are fully aware of the fact that consumers would lean towards non-transgenic food items if they had the choice, so they prefer to deprive them of this choice, proffering the argument of technical difficulties in ensuring the segregation of transgenic crops, along with the necessarily high costs involved for consumers of conventional products.

This stand cannot easily be defended, however, especially in view of the risk to which it exposes an allergy-prone consumer. 'The risk of an increase in allergies,' Arnaud Apoteker points out,

> is all the more real since people prone to food allergies know very well which food items they should avoid. But they will not be able to learn whether their allergies are due to genetically modified food items, especially in the case of food additives made from products that stem from genetic engineering.

The public left out of the equation

It appears that governments and biotechnology companies are in league against any debate on the role of GMOs in our society. As Edward Hammond puts it, 'The lack of information from official sources – government and companies – must be highlighted as an obstacle to an open debate within civil society.' In all this Bharat Dogra sees the hand of the agrochemical lobby:

> It's clear that this technology has very serious implications and that there is an urgent need to debate its various consequences before GMOs are released or marketed on a large scale. But the possibilities

of an open debate are greatly curtailed when such a technology is in the hands of commercial interests that are impatient to transform their investments into lucrative profits. Business interests act like a lobby, exerting pressure for the use of GMOs and undermining regulations and restrictions.

For Arnaud Apoteker,

> An analogy can be found here with the development of nuclear energy, which is the outcome of relatively contemporary scientific discoveries, when the public was also kept out of debates and decision-making fora precisely because of the highly technical character of this activity: the decision makers used this as a justification for keeping people in the dark, since they were considered to be incapable of understanding the technique or the stakes involved. Just as it happened in the case of nuclear energy, the possibility of military applications of genetic engineering techniques (manufacture of bacteriological weapons) could very soon lead to the policing of genetically engineered seed production facilities as a safeguard against the risks of proliferation, thereby pushing the possibility of a democratic debate on seed and food production practically out of bounds. At present, we are faced with the extremely rapid expansion of transgenic crops, without civilians having had the opportunity, at any point, of expressing their points of view or having a say in probably irreversible choices.

According to Jacques Mirenowicz, a French biologist and journalist, the deliberate wish to stifle the debate is not really surprising:

> From the moment industrial firms need continuous progress in science and technology in order to sustain their growth, it becomes logical for the management and those in responsible positions to discard all reservations with regard to what is the very bedrock of their strategies. There is no place for such criticism in the current trend of development. And it is practically impossible for any representative democracy to be representative on issues which until recently have been left out of general political discourse. Faced with increasing protests about science and technology, the public authorities of industrialised countries, to counterbalance the shortcomings of representative democracy, conduct more and more democratic participative or

deliberative (citizens are given some training on the theme being dealt with) experiments on a national level. Since GMOs constitute a formidable growth area, however, very heavy pressures weigh on such experiments – all the more so if the genetic engineering industry has a strong lobby in the country hosting such experiments. Thus, in the spring of 1998, neither the Swiss initiative 'for genetic protection' (made possible due to that country's semi-direct system of democracy) nor the French 'conference of citizens' on 'GMOs in agriculture and food' succeeded in relating the debate on GMOs to issues such as local food security or sustainable agriculture. In the first case, it was a vulgar, unruly fight between intransigent activists and scientists barricaded in zealous corporatism. In the second case, it was a highly publicised, stage-managed event on the best way to 'manage' GMOs, these being considered as an established fact. In the latter case, it was far from being a real assessment of their legitimacy in a society in which about three quarters of the population – opinion polls are clear – were against them…. The fierce competition taking place around this technology, which has barely progressed beyond the test tube stage but which public authorities seem to regard as if it were one of the last lifeboats on a sinking Titanic, in no way incites them to favour a debate that would go to the heart of the matter. Nor does it encourage them to recognise that organic farming is a credible alternative to genetic engineering in answering many of the problems caused by chemicals in agriculture. Thus, in agribusiness in particular, there is an urgent need to reconsider and reflect on the conditions that would enable the implementation of convincing experiments in deliberative democracy every time a brand new technology emerges from the laboratory. The time has come for us to stop believing that just because a discovery has been made, it must be automatically applied as if it were a divine gift not to be spurned or a natural inevitability. But how can this be done, since any criticism made in this regard comes up against a powerful administrative ideology, supported by all leaders, which seeks to harness research to high-tech innovation in the perspective of an endless spiral of economic growth? How can this be done, when any such attempt only triggers off a plethora of defensive strategies whose common aim is to neutralise any opposition, whatever its origin may be?

Mobilising farmers in developing countries

The situation is far worse in developing countries, where access to information is even more difficult. 'It is an issue of major concern that only about 20 per cent of the Southern population has an idea what GMOs are all about,' says Fred Zinanga of Zimbabwe's Community Technology Development Trust. 'Many people are likely to be caught unawares when lobbyists for transgenic plants and animals push their products into the market for their own gains.'

Awareness depends on means of communication that can alert the entire population. It is hampered by difficult living conditions that prevent farmers from fighting for anything but their own survival, as do the Saharan people featured in a report by Faisal Smati Ababsa of the National Institute of Agronomic Research (Algeria):

> There is clearly a wide gap between the world debate on GMOs and the concerns of Algeria's Oasian communities (who are completely preoccupied with their own urgent problems and needs). They are two different worlds. The debate is about modernity, of course. The level of development of two worlds has to be different. They keep falling further and further back, while the gap widens. We envy the Western world some of its debates. While the initiated confine their erudite discussions to spheres of technoscience and the international market economy – which are just unreal terms for us – Saharan farmers have to improvise pathetic strategies, from day to day, merely to defend themselves against reduced living and working areas in the painfully real world of the poor. [And because they] do not have the economic, social or political powers to develop a citizen's awareness about this danger, international civil society must manifest its solidarity more actively. Only then can we prevent firms that produce and market GMOs, who are faced with opposition in developed countries, from transferring their activities to the countries of the South that are economically and politically more fragile, as has been the case with nuclear waste, polluting industries, toxic pesticides or other experimental or declassified pharmaceutical products.

The urgent need for accountability

Today, solidarity between the countries of the North and the South is far more necessary than ever before. The development of GMOs is a worldwide phenomenon and nature knows no frontiers. As Greenpeace reminds us, 'GMOs are living organisms. They can reproduce themselves, transfer their genes and scatter themselves. They have no respect for field boundaries nor for borders between states.'[8] The transgenic problem must be dealt with on the scale of the entire planet, especially when it comes to the issue of accountability. Who will pay the damages if a herbicide-tolerant transgenic plant transmits its gene to other varieties? Who will compensate consumers if transgenic corn turns toxic? Would it be the genetic engineering company that developed the GMO, the exporting country, the importing country or the farmer? None of these concerns are seriously addressed in the Biosafety Protocol signed in January 2000.

Notes

1   Robert Horsch, Director of Technology, Monsanto, speech delivered at the 'Prince of Wales Business and the Environment Programme', Salzburg, 15 September 1997.
2   Centre of Research and Advanced Studies, National Polytechnic Institute.
3   'Les dangers du génie génétique', article published in the dossier accompanying the appeal by Greenpeace, the Confédération Paysanne, Solagral, Vétérinaires sans Frontières and several international solidarity and environment protection associations condemning the presentation of GMOs as the solution to the problem of world hunger, 1998.
4   Chris Evans, 'Permaculture Booming in Nepal', *Ileia Newsletter*, July 1997.
5   Carine Pionetti, *Semences et savoirs en Inde, diversités en péril* (Editions Cultures Croisées, December 1998).
6   Bharat Dogra, *Our Fields, Our Seeds; Farmers' Self-reliance and Protection of Land Will Help Struggle against Hunger* (New Delhi, 1998, published by the author: address and contact numbers given in Appendix 3).
7   European Commission, *Official Journal*, Nos 49–50 (2000).
8   Press dossier on the Biosafety Protocol, January 1999.

5

ABOUT ETHICS

Tampering with the Foundations of Life

'*Broader questions need to be raised about the ethics of science
in relation to greater risks of new hazards,
as well as development processes that imply the unregulated
proliferation of these hazards.*'

What if we discussed the ethics involved in the GMO debate? The question would lead to an explosive debate focusing far more on the billions of dollars invested by agro-chemical multinationals than on morals. From the violation of the laws of nature to the plundering of the natural resources of the South, however, the development of GMOs raises many questions that have to do with more than just the economics involved. 'All that can be achieved technically will be achieved, whatever be the moral costs.' Will the so-called rule of Gabor be reconfirmed? Genome engineering concerns the very secret of life and there are increasing reactions worldwide condemning the patenting of living beings or the very principle of transgenics. Like GMOs, ethics has no frontiers and the association of these two terms sounds contradictory in many cultures and systems of thought.

Transgression of the laws of nature

The difference between transgenics and transgression is a line drawn too thin to prevent humankind going one step too far. By selecting genes from one living organism and introducing them into another, we are throwing the inter-species barriers to the winds. Is it magical? Dangerous, rather. The first and foremost interest of GMOs is certainly economics. Economics get priority in international debates. The stakes involved in other fields (the law, agriculture, the environment, food, foreign exchange equity, etc.) are all related to it. What seems to be the most at stake, however, has to do with controlling the pace at which the barriers between species are being transgressed, which has been made possible by genetic engineering. The theory of evolution teaches us that the exchange of genes has been taking place between species ever since the dawn of life on earth. But these events occur rarely and are not goal-driven. Genetic engineering allows for routine transgressions aimed at specific objectives. Implications for the evolution of biological diversity are not limited to agriculture alone, but reach all of society. The production of genetically modified organisms questions the self-image and value systems of different human societies, which, in turn, question the value system of the technosciences that serve the needs of a consumer society.

For the molecular biologist, the living being has been reduced to a raw material like any other: a group of genes that can be put together as he desires and that have been put on this Earth simply to suit our needs. Playing around too much with genes brings the risk of alienating humankind from our own being as a species, something that forms the very basis of the relationship between agriculture – and our nourishment – and this Earth. Consider, too, the risks evident in recent incidents involving, among other things, mad cow disease, hormone-enhanced bulls, pigs and antibiotics, or chicken and dioxin. 'By working with genes, tinkering with the very matter of the living being and marketing it, the agricultural world is identifying itself more and more with the industrial world and is losing the specific relationship it enjoys with the living world,' is Arnaud Apoteker's verdict.

> Crops are no longer plant species, but molecule-producing units. The farmer becomes a 'moleculturist', a skilled labourer on the assembly line producing nutritive or pharmaceutical substances. An increasingly urbanised society is moving further and further away from nature, gradually losing the notion of the role of agriculture in its food production and of the relationship between the field and the plate.

Science serving profit

What is the purpose of all this? 'Companies are directing biotechnology along the path that promises the highest and fastest profits. Their strategy shows little concern for human and social well being,' says Bharat Dogra.

Many companies involved with GMOs are also active in the agrochemical industry and their first and foremost efforts are directed at promoting the sales of their herbicides.

It is certainly not by accident that most transgenic crops marketed today contain a herbicide-resisting gene. The major hi-tech companies dealing with life sciences are, in fact, the biggest producers of chemical products. For them, GMOs are part of a strategy that enables them to market their pesticide production. In less than ten years, DuPont (a world leader in chemicals), Novartis (a world leader in plant protection products) and others including Aventis (a merger of Hoechst and Rhône-Poulenc) or AstraZeneca (a major pharmaceutical and agro-chemical group), have all established a major 'life sciences' position.

The most ironic example is perhaps that of Monsanto. In the course of the last few years, this American multinational spent billions of dollars in taking over many seed production and biotechnology companies. It is true that for a world GMO campaign leader, time is money. The patent for RoundUp, its leading product that generates considerable profits, expires in the year 2000 in most countries. This will then enable its competitors to market similar products. With this deadline in mind, Monsanto has developed transgenic crops that are resistant to RoundUp. Along with this, farmers buying their seeds are contractually obliged to use this herbicide on their land. Cunning, isn't it? This is why it is difficult to believe the loud Monsanto claims that GMOs help fight hunger in the world.

Seizing the living

This is all the more striking when we see that Monsanto's marketing offensive is accompanied by an extensive operation for privatising the living being (see Chapter 7). In the early 1980s, a universal taboo was destroyed when the United States Supreme Court decided to grant a patent on a living organism for the first time in the history of humanity. Since then, biotechnology companies have embarked upon a frantic race to procure patents on genetically modified micro-organisms, plants and animals. This 'patent mania' brings several ethical problems to the fore. Aren't living beings public property? Don't living beings belong to a common and intergenerational world heritage? Can they be privatised like any other invention?

'For many religious and cultural traditions, extending patents to living organisms is intrinsically unacceptable,' affirms Geoff Tansey, a food policy specialist, in a report entitled 'Trade, Intellectual Property, Food and Biological Diversity'. 'More specifically, claiming that it is a human invention when you are dealing with a living being violates the conscience of those who believe that there is a divine creator and that life is a gift, a common heritage shared by humanists.'[1] Jean-Pierre Berlan vividly endorses this view:

> The living being reproduces and multiplies in the farmer's field. This fundamental faculty of the living being belongs to everyone – just like sunlight and the air we breathe. It is the very foundation of our individual and collective existence. In the name of progress and competition – in other words, the huge profits privatisation reaps from what is the common property of humanity – our societies are in the process of confiscating [life] and transforming it into the prerogative of just a few major companies. Granting such a prerogative is like barring our doors and windows against natural light to allow candle sellers to sell us their wares. It makes farmers thieves and citizens receivers of stolen goods.[2]

The patenting of living beings sets a new marketing trend in our society, where everything – or almost everything – can be bought or sold. Geoff Tansey again:

> Patenting life forms constitutes a significant progress in the larger process which wants to transform life into a marketable product and reduce the value of life and nature to a simple economic expression. Patent laws represent the balance that society has established between the principle of compensation for inventiveness in a commercial and competitive culture, and the principle of making the knowledge drawn from research available, free of cost. However, due to increasing privatisation, scientific research seems to be turning its back on the traditional values of discussion and open debate, turning, rather, towards confidentiality and secrets. As a consequence, it is to be feared that with the increasing power of companies, the grant of patents to living forms may destroy an already unsound equilibrium and further strengthen the power of companies, while marginalising

issues like human well-being and social justice even more. Some groups have appealed for a total rethinking of the way in which innovations in agriculture and life sciences are being promoted.[3]

The long-term danger is that one day the planet's food could become completely dependent on the legal privilege granted to just a few companies. 'Have we thought about the historically exorbitant price that has to be paid for privatised genetic progress? Who will keep a check on the monopoly that we are willing to give to some multinational companies?' asks Jean-Pierre Berlan.[4] If we pursue this reasoning to the end, we will develop a society that flouts fundamental rights. Farmers are already experiencing the consequences of the privatisation of natural resources that belong to the entire planet. Their freedom and independence are shrinking fast with the marketing of transgenic crops that are subjected to very strict conditions. For example, farmers who buy RoundUp-resistant soya bean seeds do not have the right to use other herbicides. Nor can they keep their seeds to replant them the following year, or exchange them with their neighbours. What is even worse, Monsanto hires detectives to supervise farmers and check that they are not keeping back a part of their harvest for sowing the following year. If they do, watch out for the strong arm of the 'law'! The violators have to destroy their produce and pay damages to the American corporate giant. All this simply for having given a living being the opportunity to reproduce.

Imbalance in North–South relations

Such abuse is even more blatant in developing countries. For here the patenting of living beings is accompanied by a positive plundering of knowledge and of a unique plant heritage. Some see it as a new form of colonialism and plundering of the resources of the Third World. Biotech companies that patent certain plant varieties, without financially compensating the local farmers, deprive them of the fruit of their labour. For, from generation to generation, it is the farmers who have maintained this rich biodiversity, not found anywhere else in the world. 'In industrialised countries, patents are granted to breeders with the aim of protecting the creation of new cultivars. This practice is totally unjust towards the countries of the South,' declares Kakule Kasonia, a Congolese scientist working for a Belgian data bank dedicated to traditional veterinary medicine.

In fact, the latter contribute tremendously to seed and gene banks, but are denied the use of them. Once they have been crossed with other varieties, varieties that have been naturalised, cultivated, and improved by generations of farmers from the South are protected by patents and resold at exorbitant rates to their country of origin, as if they were new and different varieties, without taking into account the efforts of generations of farmers who had earlier contributed to improving these varieties.

The mismatch of power between countries of the South and North ensures that 'the equitable international convention' desired by Kakule Kasonia will certainly not take place tomorrow. Negotiations held on the WTO's Agreement on Trade Related Aspects of Intellectual Property Rights (TRIPS) were dominated by industrial powers whose aim was to protect the interest of their companies at the expense of the rights of rural communities (see Chapter 7). 'A just and equitable negotiation process is desirable for the international trade agreements to work in the long term,' says Geoff Tansey.

Moreover, the legitimacy of a rule-based system depends on it being equally accessible to all its members. Presently, the differences in resources and capacity levels between the negotiating parties are too marked. Therefore, many observers feel that it is difficult to consider all World Trade Organisation members as equally capable of participating in negotiations or benefiting equitably from the dispute settlement procedure. In such conditions, it is unlikely that any final agreement will represent a fair balance of interests. Much needs to be done to establish an equitable system of negotiations that will not be dominated excessively by a few powerful countries, which are themselves strongly influenced by the industrial sector.[5]

Ethics committees under pressure

And where do ethics fit in all this? There is hardly any room for
ethical considerations in societies where the doors of democratic
debate have been closed, where GMOs prevail even before civil
society has had an opportunity to raise its voice (see Chapter 4). In
France, as in many other countries, ethical questioning has been delib-
erately limited to the *ad hoc* committees set up in the 1980s. According
to Jacques Mirenowicz, these ethical committees are not able to play
the critical role assigned to them satisfactorily:

> For a long time, particularly after 1945, we wanted to believe that
> new technologies would remain as neutral as GDP figures, or else that
> they would only have a beneficial effect. Then, in the 1970s, labora-
> tories started to create medical complications that necessitated, in the
> urgency of the situation, a serious takeover by the authorities. The
> advent of the first 'test-tube baby' in 1978 shook the field of ethics – a
> branch of philosophy that was not particularly active at that time –
> and gave it a new lease of life. In the 1980s, facing the same phenom-
> enon, all the industrialised countries set up ethics committees (or
> commissions that played a similar role) with the aim of producing
> consultative documents and recommendations. They were sometimes
> even given an educational responsibility regarding practices that
> involved value conflicts stemming from the technology boom in life
> sciences.... These committees can be criticised for at least three
> reasons, however, of which the third one seems to be the most funda-
> mental: (1) numerous scientists, who are thus both judges and affected
> parties, are members of these committees. Inevitably, their interests
> coincide with those of their peers, whose research conditions and
> possibilities depend on the current legislation; (2) in order to legislate,
> parliamentarians have to assume the responsibility of thinking about
> the effects – particularly the subjective effects – of the rapid progress
> in science and technology. But experience shows that the opinions
> expressed by national ethics committees often end up as laws (a
> phenomenon that can clearly be seen in France). By reappropriating
> the opinions of these committees, parliamentarians give them a para-
> legislative role that short-circuits democracy; (3) ethics committee

members represent the parties that are directly involved in the matter under consideration. As the engineer and philosopher, Michel Tibon-Cornillot, puts it, ethics committees represent a 'coordinated and homogenous' culture. They are 'the products of an advancing industrial society. Its members are obviously its heralds, since they are, by definition, part of those to whom this society gives the opportunity to express themselves.' In the light of these three objections, ethics committees cannot play the critical role that this epoch desperately needs. Their deliberations fall in line with – and strengthen – the dominant reasoning to which they adhere. This too is another way of closing the doors of democratic debate on science and technology.[6]

Outcry from the four corners of the earth

Fortunately, the doors cannot be completely closed and voices are being raised against the patenting of living material. Very lively debates on the rules and regulations concerning the patenting of living beings are presently taking place in civil society (professional organisations of doctors, farmers, consumer associations, sectoral associations, NGOs, environmental groups and others). These debates are taking place everywhere in the world, and voice enormous opposition to regulations that seem fundamentally unjust and/or flout the inherent dignity of the living being. Others, more harsh, denounce not just the multinational takeover of the planet's heritage, but also the very principle of transgenics. 'We reject genetic engineering which is today built on the absence of ethics and which violates human integrity. These techniques do not guarantee the safety of human life, or that of the animal and plant species that have been living on Earth for millions of years,' declared the fifty indigenous farmers' organisations and environmental groups that met at Quito (Ecuador) in January 1999. 'This technology is the logical and distorted part of a global development process based on inequalities between regions and the exploitation of human beings and nature. It is the subordination of the agricultural and traditional economies of developing countries to the enormous appetite of gigantic agro-industrial international groups.'[7]

Genes of the Mind and Genes of the Heart

Issiaka-Prosper Laleye, Professor of Epistemology and Anthropology at the University of Gaston Berger de Saint-Louis in Senegal, offers an 'anti-reductionist approach' to genetically modified organisms.

From an anthropological point of view – in the perspective, that is, of human understanding – the fact that humans are capable of modifying the living being at the level of his genes is in itself an imposing phenomenon, which should always be granted its rightful dimensions. This will not be easy: the dimensions are imposing, and imposing phenomena are not an everyday thing.

In reflecting on the rights of rural communities with regard to GMOs, we are not dealing with the root causes of the GMO phenomenon. If it were so, we would have asked first which gene(s) and which genetic engineering – carried out by whom and when – made us capable of doing such things, as human beings. Instead, we limit ourselves to dealing with some of the major consequences of the GMO phenomenon, looking into a few of the numberless mechanisms which are instilling in our societies and their cultures – imperceptibly but surely, and for a long time – what can already be called the GMO era.

Focusing on laws, we are inclined to neglect the metaphysical or spiritual dimensions of the GMO phenomenon on the one hand, and its ethical dimensions on the other. Yet, what is a law worth if it has no spiritual inspiration and no underlying moral design? Or rather, to be more precise, what is a law worth that does not want to, does not dare to, or is unable to examine its own spiritual base, or is not concerned with the moral principles on which it is founded and the moral rules that it establishes? ...

If it is not easy to think about the rights of rural communities in the face of GMOs, and even more difficult to act in favour of these communities, this is because our world operates on a rationale of permanent marginalisation that continuously pushes certain categories of people away from power, training and education, health, leisure and even spirituality. Thus poverty in all its forms remains an apparently insoluble problem in our world. For although our world already has the objective means to overcome certain aspects of poverty, we remain spiritually or morally unable to use these means.

Let us look at the three dimensions of the GMO question which, for the time being, make it very difficult for any effective measures to be taken in favour of rural communities. The first dimension is scientific or even techno-scientific. The second is political or even socio-political, for everywhere fundamentally political provisions and considerations control the granting of techno-scientific means. The third dimension is commercial, since genetic modifications are applied to 'things' that are already included in the trade networks of national and international goods and services, and these commercial networks hold and keep all humanity in their mesh.

Rural communities are marginalised by our policies, our sciences and our global trade agreements. I do not mean to say that no one thinks of rural communities or talks about them at these three levels. Indeed, everyone seems to be talking about them.Paradoxically, if rural communities are today a major focus of attention, it is because they were forced out of the centre of the world a long time ago. And this is simply – but also tragically, one must say – because our world functions by pushing them out to the periphery....

This is obviously as much a question of knowledge as one of action. I do not wish to consider it as an isolated individual but as a member and leader of a multi-disciplinary team which has taken up the task of studying all changes affecting the rural sub-Saharan world in black Africa. The group is Equipe de recherche sur les mutations du rural sahélien (ERMURS), a research group on changes in rural sub-Saharan regions. It proposes to establish a centre for the study of social and natural biodiversity at the new Gaston Berger University in Saint-Louis, Senegal.

The centre's main tasks would be to learn about biodiversity, and to train and educate rural sub-Saharan communities in this subject. The object would be to extend know-how, respect, conservation and use of the genetic animal, plant and socio-cultural heritage in order to consolidate and safeguard natural and social biodiversity – not to speak of human biodiversity. Thus thought and action would contribute to bringing about changes in some of the genes of our understanding, our hearts and our minds so that genetic engineering could truly benefit humanity – the human in its entirety and all human beings.

Notes

1 Geoff Tansey, 'Trade, Intellectual Property, Food and Biological Diversity; Key Choices and Questions within the Framework of a Re-examination, in 1999, of Article 27.3(b) Dealing with the Agreement on Trade Related Aspects of Intellectual Property Rights (TRIPS)', drafted for the Quaker Committee for Peace and Service, London, February 1999.

2 Jean-Pierre Berlan, 'Turning Farmers into "Pirates" and Citizens into "Receivers of Stolen Goods"?' Article published in the file accompanying the appeal by Greenpeace in collaboration with the Confédération Paysanne, Solagral, Vétérinaires sans Frontières and several international solidarity and environment protection associations denouncing the presentation of GMOs as a solution to the problem of hunger, 1998.

3 Geoff Tansey, 'Trade, Intellectual Property, Food and Biological Diversity'.

4 Jeane-Pierre Berlan, 'Turning Farmers into "Pirates" '.

5. Geoff Tansey, 'Trade, Intellectual Property, Food and Biological Diversity'.

6 J. Mirenowicz, 'Towards a Renewal of the Social and Scientific Contract', presentation at preparatory seminar organised by the Charles Léopold Mayer Foundation, Villarceaux (France), 22–23 April 1999, before the Science Conference, Budapest, 26 June–1 July 1999.

7 Latin American declaration on transgenic organisms by farmers' and other indigenous Latin American organisations, Quito, 22 January 1999.

6

MORATORIUM
ON COMMERCIALISATION
Setting the Rules

'A moratorium should be imposed on the commercialisation of GMOs until it has been proved that they have no detrimental effects on environment and health. If any GMOs are commercialised, after satisfying all safety norms, it should be ensured that they reinforce true food security and sustainable agricultural systems.'

It is imperative to wait. It is imperative because we still do not know the effects of GMOs on the environment and our own health. It is imperative because genetic pollution is irreversible. It is imperative because agro-chemical multinationals develop and market their products so rapidly that civilians and government regulations fail to keep pace with them. A moratorium is therefore imperative, as is reflection on the strategies to be adopted to fight against the unruly development of GMOs.

The indispensable moratorium

If one thing is certain about the effects of a generalised use of GMOs, it is that we know nothing. Arnaud Apoteker reminds us that

> We are incapable of foreseeing the series of events that will take place if GMOs are introduced into the environment right from the gene stage to the ecosystem. The ecological issues at stake are most complex and the timescale for these phenomena is much longer than the calendar set by multinationals to get back returns on its investments and the electoral mandates of politicians.[1]

And the few trials which have been conducted so far will not help us to see things better. 'It is impossible to extend the results of experiments conducted in laboratories on a small scale to extremely complex ecosystems or commercial products,' explains Vandana Shiva, Director of the Institute of Science, Technology and Ecology in New Delhi in an article published by the *Guardian*.[2]

> The tests conducted on experimental plants evaluate the risks on plants alone. They do not enable us to draw conclusions on the over-all effects of commercial cultures on the environment. Genetic

engineering is not an exact science. It is a technology that is full of
uncertainty and imperfection. Just because it has become possible to
manipulate genes individually, it does not mean that we know exactly
how GMOs behave. Gene transfer can have unforeseeable consequences as plants and biological organisms evolve continuously.

The risks are very real. They may concern ecology (gene flow,
insect resistance, reduced biodiversity, etc.) or health (development of
resistance to antibiotics, allergies, etc.). Though we are still not sure of
anything, each week brings its share of findings which only increase
our suspicions regarding the so-called harmlessness of GMOs (see
Chapter 3). Under these conditions, is it really necessary to continue
the commercial cultivation of transgenic plants? Should we take the
risk of seeing our 'baseless' fears proved right, one by one? For a
number of scientists, the answer is very clear: 'No', all the more so
since the damage done would be irreparable. Apoteker points out that

> The main characteristic of a possible 'genetic pollution' is that it is
> irreversible as opposed to all other types of pollution that we are
> familiar with. In fact, transgenesis is done with living organisms. They
> are then released into the environment where they live, reproduce,
> multiply, mutate, invade other ecosystems, etc. Chemical pollution is
> arrested the moment the chemical activity stops; radioactive pollution
> too, even though it takes several thousands of years. But, genetic
> pollution is irreversible. Once a gene 'escapes' into nature, say in the
> form of a harmful plant species, it cannot be brought back to the labo-
> ratory when its effects start showing.

Who will pay when this scenario becomes real? Who will reim-
burse the farmer who loses a part of his crop because the insects have
become resistant to the insecticides that he normally used? At this
point, we have no answer. No legal responsibility has been defined.
On the one hand, scientists admit their ignorance regarding the
'unforeseeable consequences' of GMOs, and on the other even legal
practitioners are helpless against the new generation of 'products'.
Everything seems to stem from the urge for profit displayed by a few
multinationals holding everyone, even governments, to ransom. This

is why, as Arnaud Trollé and Robert Ali Brac de la Perrière show in
The Transgenic Trap, we need to pause and decree a moratorium:

> Changes in this sector are taking place at such a breakneck speed that
> no one, except perhaps a few powerful firms, is able to control them.
> Genetic engineering of plants, which was still an emerging field only a
> decade back, is today infused with investments from a number of big
> private firms, and revolutionary biotechnological innovations are
> churned out. For example, the patent for Terminator technology, a
> genetic mechanism that sterilises seeds, was filed in March 1998. In all
> probability, it is a technology that will have highly detrimental conse-
> quences on the autonomy of farmers and breeders in the coming
> decade. Several other such innovations are being worked on in labora-
> tories without any concern for the economic and social fall-out in the
> field of agro-foods. All other players, who are lagging behind, are
> worried about what else is in store, more so because even legislators
> seem to find no way of controlling the potential consequences of trans-
> genic products on agriculture. In this way, the market of biotechno-
> logical innovations is hurtling society into a no-law area as there isn't
> enough time to formulate any law. Faced with such a situation, the
> only alternative for society to arrest this threat is to impose a morato-
> rium on all genetic engineering applications in agriculture till the
> social conditions required for its acceptance are collectively formed.[3]

A moratorium is not only desirable but also possible as the only
urgency seems to be the biotech firms' anxiety to reap good returns at
the earliest. GMOs are not, as is claimed, a solution to the problem of
hunger in the world. It is therefore critical to wait, take time to
organise debates, set up a suitable regulatory framework and then
proceed. The keyword here is caution. The strategy is nothing short
of that dictated by the precautionary principle.

The European Union has decided, in fact, to implement that
principle. Towards the end of June 1999, the environment ministers
of the European Union imposed a moratorium on the commercialisation of new varieties of GMOs until 2002, in spite of differences
between the 15 member countries. The first group – Austria, Belgium,
Germany, Finland, the Netherlands and Sweden – declared their

'intention of not authorising the commercialisation of GMOs until it was proved that they would have no negative effects on environment and health' The second, more radical group consisting of France, Greece, Italy, Denmark and Luxembourg, confirmed that until there was regulation 'guaranteeing labelling and effective traceability of GMOs and its derivative products', they would act to 'suspend the new authorisations for cultivation and marketing'. Since these five countries represent a blocking minority in the committees handling the subject, the adoption of new authorisations can be prevented. The European Union is therefore committed to a moratorium until 2002, at which time the new European directive regulating the procedure for GMO authorisation in Europe will come into force. The United States and other countries producing transgenic plants are yet to be convinced that they need to adopt a similar position: a real struggle may lie ahead.

Beyond the moratorium

Imposing a moratorium will be beneficial but insufficient. Farmers' associations and allied organisations should fight on other fronts too. Some of the speakers at the Rishikesh seminar presented their thoughts on multi-pronged strategies.

Staking the claims

'The first, in terms of oppositional politics, is to campaign actively on these issues and to lobby governments, institutions and the industry itself to reform their policies and practices', explains Neil Ritchie.

In addition, we must continue to demand that our government guard our long-term health and environment and make investments in research that serve the public good, not the interests of private capital. We must also continue to demand that government policies make it possible for farmers to earn a living wage while acting as stewards of the land. We must demand that consumers be given adequate information through labelling and disclosure to make informed decisions. And we must continue to encourage other NGO partners and governments to resist the US pressure to accept systems that defend the interests of corporations over people.

These demands should also require the definition of responsibilities with regard to risks and the independence and multi-disciplinary nature of expert commissions which grant approvals for the commercialisation of GMOs. Peter Muchambo from APM Africa thinks that steps should also be taken to put pressure on corporations. This can be done through the creation of

> a body which can play a critical role in monitoring and mediating between farmers and the agribusiness corporations. In practice, such a body would identify areas of conflicts and challenge the company involved. If the company proves difficult, this body can then call for a world-wide ban on their products.

Such an organisation could also undertake the verification of seeds to ensure that they had not been genetically modified.

> Multinational agro-seed companies have subsidiaries in almost all countries in the world and are therefore in a position to introduce GMO technology in those countries secretly. There is practically no way of knowing whether the seed being advertised to the poor farmers is the 'terminator' or 'verminator'. So it is important that they can send samples to a monitoring body which can determine the level of toxic material in our soils. This organisation could also investigate or supply information on any topic.

Promoting sustainable agriculture

'The second approach, a more constructive type of politics and practices, is to create alternatives that directly create and support alternative forms of production, distribution and exchange,' Ritchie suggests.

> These would include supporting food cooperatives and smaller retail outlets; supporting seed exchange networks; purchasing locally grown and organic produce whenever possible; forming direct links between farmers and communities; and growing and preparing our own food whenever possible.

It is also necessary to look for markets which promote non-GMO products; to propose new orientations for agricultural research in order to make it possible to adapt breeding – and genetic engineering – to the needs of the farmers facing problems such as salinification and drought; and to analyse the means to minimise dependence on chemical inputs and to defend the choice of sustainable agriculture.

Continuously spreading information

The third battle concerns information. 'Do we have people or organisations that specialise in raising alarm bells at all levels – be it at the grassroots level or the offices of the United Nations Secretary General?' asks Peter Muchambo.

> In saying this, I know there are RAFI, IATP and a few other organisations involved in monitoring and disseminating information and knowledge, but it can be argued that they are a drop in the ocean.... What other mechanisms can be worked out to keep everybody informed regardless of caste, colour, creed, sex, rich or poor ?... It is the Third World countries that are going to suffer more because of lack of adequate information and in some cases of poverty. Knowledge and information should be disseminated widely to inform farmers especially about the harmful effects of GMO technology on their soils and environment. This can be done by organising more workshops where farmers can be exposed to information on GMOs. This can help them specially to take a position for or against the perpetrators.... We have to find ways of increasing the circulation of newsletters so as to improve people's access to information on biotechnology. In Zimbabwe, the APM Network has already started doing something about it and is reproducing relevant newsletters for our subsistence farmers in remote areas.... Electronic and print media journalists also need to be exposed regularly to updated information on GMOs to help them produce accurate reports.

Finally, it is essential that farmers come to understand clearly the changes and threats posed by GMOs through a concrete exchange of experience, and assist farmers' organisations in tackling this complex and ever-changing issue. This assistance could materialise through the founding of a research centre which would bring together biologists, legal experts and economists to ensure proper monitoring of GMOs and to raise awareness of their impact. Monitoring is already undertaken by NGOs such as RAFI and the Union of Concerned Scientists (UCS) in the US, and GRAIN and Ecoropa in Europe. It needs to be developed further.

Notes

1   Arnaud Apoteker, 'Les dangers du génie génétique', article published in a report accompanying the appeal made by Greenpeace, Confédération Paysanne, Solagral, Vétérinaires sans Frontières and numerous associations of international solidarity and environmental protection to denounce the projection of GMOs as a solution to hunger, 1998.

2   As quoted in *Courrier International*, No. 381, 19–25 February 1998.

3   Robert Ali Brac de la Perrière and Arnaud Trollé, *The Transgenic Trap: on Bridging Research and Agriculture* (Paris: Charles Léopold Mayer Publications, 1999).

7

THE BATTLE OVER
INTELLECTUAL PROPERTY RIGHTS

Living Matter Turned into
Private Property

'The rights of farming communities should be fully protected within the
framework of the WTO Agreement on Trade Related Aspects of
Intellectual Property Rights (TRIPS). These rights should include the
rights of farmers as innovators and preservers of seeds.'

'When amending patent laws in accordance with the TRIPS Agreement,
provisions of section 2 of Article 27 of the
TRIPS Agreement can be used as it allows members to
"exclude from patentability, any invention that might be perceived
as detrimental to public order and morality if commercialised on their
territory. This includes any threat to human, animal and plant
safety or serious prejudice to the environment ...".'

Can a living being be patented? Yes, say a number of industrialised countries, without any hesitation. Led by the United States, they are pressuring the developing countries to set up systems for protecting intellectual property rights (IPR) on all inventions. The supporters of patents won their first battle by making the World Trade Organisation (WTO) adopt the Agreement on Trade Related Aspects of Intellectual Property Rights (TRIPS). The countries of the South have until 2005, at the latest, to incorporate into their national law the granting of patents 'for any invention, product or process, in all technological fields'.

Everything, it seems, is up for grabs. When it comes to the creation of plant varieties, countries have the choice between two IPR protection systems: patents or *sui generis,* the latter being a more flexible system designed according to each country's needs. That is the theory: in practice, however, the countries of the North are encouraging those of the South to adopt the *sui generis* system of the Union for the Protection of New Varieties of Plants (UPOV), which gives the breeders, much to the detriment of farmers, certain rights comparable to those of patents. The problem here is that UPOV, like the WTO agreement, is in contradiction with the spirit of the Convention on Biological Diversity (CBD). Whereas TRIPS and UPOV aim at imposing exclusive private intellectual property rights on biodiversity, the CBD, adopted in 1992 by 170 countries at the Earth Summit in Rio (Brazil), recognises the collective rights of communities to this very resource.

Numerous countries wish to depart from this Convention in designing a *sui generis* system that would protect the rights of their rural communities over plant resources. The revision of the TRIPS agreement, which starts in 2000, will give them their last chance to express their point of view. The prospect of victory, however, is still remote.

In the beginning was the patent

IPR: these three letters play a central role in the debate on genetically modified organisms. Under the three letters lurks a subject that places the industrialised nations and the developing countries at loggerheads with each other. Intellectual property rights are the rights granted by a state authority to individual and legal entities for the fruits of intellectual effort. The development of GMOs depends largely on the judicial protection systems of IPR (whether of the patent type[1] or others). 'Corporations do not resort to genetic engineering to modify plants or animals unless they can recover their investments in research and development,' explains Geoff Tansey, a food policy specialist:[2]

> Since new plant varieties and a number of biotech products are all living organisms which can reproduce, it is not necessary to keep buying them. In order to ensure returns on investments and a flow of revenue in future on these inventions, corporations want to extend IPR, more particularly patents, world-wide to cover the original material and the following generations of the newly invented forms of life such as plant varieties.

The attack is two-pronged: economic and social. If all countries adhered to industrial patent rights for genetically modified plants, the patents could be globalised very quickly. On the other hand, the adoption of the *sui generis* system,[3] which is different from patent laws and takes into account the rights of rural communities, can block the distribution of GMOs.

Biotechnology companies have taken the first step by making some countries accept patenting of living beings. The US Supreme Court broke the barrier in 1980 by ruling for the first time, in a case on bacteria that acquired the capacity to reduce hydrocarbons through genetic engineering, that it is possible to patent living organisms. Since then, other countries have followed the US lead. Even the European Union adopted a directive in 1998 on the protection of biotechnological inventions, thereby legalising the patenting of living organisms. But there is a chasm separating the countries of the North from those of the South. The former are very attached to their intellectual property and have thus set up legislation protecting inventions and followed biotechnological evolution by recognising the patenting of living organisms. The latter, on the other hand, are less concerned with the problem as they have few or no innovative firms, and therefore most of them do not have a legal system which protects IPR. Much to the displeasure of Western multinationals, a patent protects the inventor only in the country or countries in which it was granted. According to Washington, this judicial gap encourages the trade of pirated products. It estimates, for example, the amount of royalties lost by American companies through the unauthorised use of its patents to produce fertilisers by countries of the South at US$200 million. Thus, the industrialised nations benefited a great deal from the decision taken at the Uruguay round of talks on GATT, which preceded the creation of the World Trade Organisation, to 'impose' the drawing up of an agreement on TRIPS. This agreement, which came into force on 1 January 1995, makes it binding on the member countries to grant patents 'for all inventions, products and processes, in all technological fields provided they are new, involve a new step and are capable of industrial application'. *All* inventions, including those based on living material.

Article 27 of the WTO Agreement on the Trade Related Aspects of Intellectual Property Rights

Section 5 : Patents

1   Subject to the provisions of paragraphs 2 and 3, patents shall be available for any inventions, whether products or processes, in all fields of technology, provided that they are new, involve a new step and are capable of industrial application. Subject to paragraph 4 of Article 65, paragraph 8 of Article 70 and paragraph 3 of this Article, patents shall be available and patent rights enjoyable without discrimination as to the

place of invention or field of technology and as to whether products are imported or locally produced.

2 Members may exclude from patentability any invention that might be perceived as detrimental to public order and morality if commercialised on their territory. This includes any threat to human, animal and plant safety or serious prejudice to the environment. However, such an exclusion must not be made merely because the commercialisation is prohibited by their national law.

3 Members may also exclude from patentability:
   a) diagnostic, therapeutic and surgical methods for the treatment of humans or animals;
   b) plants and animals other than micro-organisms, and essentially biological processes for the production of plants or animals other than non-biological and microbiological processes. However, Members shall provide for the protection of plant varieties either with patents or with an effective *sui generis* system or with any combination thereof. The provisions of this subparagraph shall be reviewed four years after the date of entry into force of the WTO Agreement.

The developed countries had to apply the provisions of the agreement within the period of a year. Developing countries have until 1 January 2000. The least developed countries were given a time period of ten years. But dissent is being expressed in the South. Sure enough, Article 27.3 (b) grants states the possibility of 'excluding from patentability plants and animals other than micro-organisms'. But, by so doing, it legalises the patenting of life since it authorises members to grant patents on plants and animals. Further, the agreement is very strict on the protection of intellectual property rights over plant varieties (varieties developed by professional breeders). This very article 27.3 (b) indeed forces member countries to provide for 'the protection of plant varieties either by patents or by a *sui generis* system [meaning a system adapted to their own context] or by any combination thereof'. In other words, any state is allowed to prohibit the patenting of a 'non-modified' plant but it absolutely must protect the intellectual property rights of an inventor who has crafted a plant variety, by, for instance, inserting a foreign gene into a plant. Whether they like it or not, developing countries will have to enforce this legislation – 'as soon as possible', insist the advocates of patents on life, headed by the United States. 'The pressure to extend the legislation to IPR related to biodiversity in developing countries is growing stronger,' say GRAIN and the Gaia Foundation.[4]

> For some countries, that would mean being on the Super 301 of the 'surveillance list' of the US which blacklists the 'bad players' of free trade. For others, the pressure comes from the ministries of commerce which are responsible for applying the agreement signed at the end of the Uruguay round of talks. Practically all over the world, it is said that patents and other forms of IPR are essential assets to stimulate investments in biotechnology, which in turn help the economy and improve food security. This argument is completely fallacious. The only justification for this world-wide campaign in favour of IPR is the increase in profits for the transnational firms based in the North.

More patents = less innovation?

Indeed, nothing proves that greater protection of IPR spurs investment, explain GRAIN and Gaia.

> Contrary to what firms say, there is no positive correlation between the possibility of access to IPR and the scope of research and development from one country to the other. The Chinese are the most advanced rice breeders even though they do not have any form of protection on new plant varieties. On the other hand, in the US, protection led to an increase in improvement programmes for only two plant species. The rare studies that were conducted in countries where

the protection of vegetal breeding has existed for decades, like the US, show that this type of legal system had several consequences: a low stimulus impact on plant improvement, reduced information and genetic material exchange between the private sector and the public sector, a reduced role of the public sector in plant improvement, and an increase in the price of seeds sold to farmers.

In fact, it appears that by restraining the free circulation of new knowledge, the generalised application of patents hampers rather than encourages research. Because of patents on GMOs, the circulation of genetic resources is gradually coming to a standstill – not only between countries of the North and the South, but also amongst research groups in the Northern countries which are competing against each other in the race to acquire the rights over a genome. In this race, the public sector inevitably falls behind and depends more and more on major groups working in the field of agrochemistry. Kakule Kasonia, whose organisation has constructed a data bank on traditional African veterinary medicine, shares this view.

The appropriation of germplasm and the privatisation of research on the improvement of cultivated plants make access to knowledge and technical know-how even more difficult, especially in the countries of the South. Instead of promoting free trade, privatisation promotes secrecy and tends to increase dependence in the field of technology.

Fred Zinanga of CTDT is also concerned about the consequences of TRIPS in Third World countries:

Agricultural development in the South is likely to be hampered as developed countries continue to further their biotechnologies.... The General Agreement on Tariffs and Trade (GATT) and its adjunct Trade Related Aspects of Intellectual Property Rights (TRIPS) are causing much concern throughout the countries of the South, most of whose economies are agro-based, in combination with the World Trade Organisation (WTO) trade regime.... The TRIPS agreement fails to protect the genetic resource of the South while allowing genetically modified materials to be patented.

Patents or *sui generis*?

Whatever the case may be, the time has come for developing nations to make a choice between patents or an appropriate *sui generis* system. Legal protection of IPR based on patents is much too restrictive as it gives the holder the right to prevent anyone from using his invention for any purpose, including research and reproduction, unless royalties are paid. Farmers who use patented seeds do not therefore have the right to keep a part of their harvest for replanting during the next season unless they pay a fee. They cannot even cross a patented plant with another plant in order to improve it. GRAIN and Gaia warn that

> Countries which choose to extend their patent laws to plant varieties will in fact be setting up a system of private rights allowing some individuals to prevent others from reproducing, using or selling the protected variety or any product that is likely to contain patented genetic information. Who will benefit from this? Farmers can neither freely access nor use seeds. Scientists will face restrictions in their research on the use of patented material. Moreover, private rights reduce the availability of biodiversity and threaten the future of public research.

The second solution, *sui generis*, is a system of legal rights specially adapted to 'inventions' which are different from standard IPR protection schemes such as patents and copyrights. In this way the TRIPS agreement offers member countries the possibility of defining a particular regulation to protect intellectual property on plant varieties 'efficiently'. But can developing countries really define their own rules of the game? Not really. The seed lobby within the WTO is pushing them to adopt the rights of the Union for Protection of New Plant Varieties, a *sui generis* system that it has singled out – in what may seem a rather contradictory fashion – from many others. 'The WTO is presently sponsoring a series of meetings[5] within developing countries with the cooperation of UPOV and the World Intellectual Property Organisation,' states Johnson A. Ekpere, consultant for the scientific, technical and research commission of the Organisation for African Unity (OAU) in a paper distributed at one of the meetings.[6]

These meetings are organised to discuss the manner in which the
concerned countries will implement the WTO directives with regard
to biodiversity within the framework of the TRIPS Agreement....
The theme of these regional workshops ... actually harbours a specific
objective: to persuade governments that UPOV 78 and UPOV 91 are
ultimately the ideal solution to the obligations imposed by TRIPS. It
is perhaps the ideal solution for most of the developed countries but is
difficult to implement and far from beneficial for developing countries
in general, and Africa in particular.

What is a Good *Sui Generis* System?

*Geoff Tansey, specialist in food policies, considers the requirements of an
effective* sui generis *system.*[7]

The country must define the extent of the system. This should
cover:

- *that which is protected* (i.e., it must define the 'plant variety');

- *the conditions in which the protection is given* – whether it responds
  to the criteria of novelty or invention as defined by the legislation on patents, or the criteria of distinctive character, uniformity and stability (DUS) covered by the legislation
  regarding breeding rights, or to a modified version of these
  criteria for protecting more heterogeneous varieties. The
  country must define whether or not it should include additional criteria such as the declaration of origin and value for
  cultivation and utilisation;

- *the extent of the rights given*, specified by
  - the list of acts requiring the authorisation of the rights
    holder (sale, production, importation, etc.);

- the definition of material that these acts cover (propagation material of reproductive origin and/or vegetal origin, materials harvested, etc.);
- the exceptions to this right (such as exception for research, exception in favour of the breeder, and exception in favour of the farmer);

- *The validity of the right*, which could be any lapse in time considered economically appropriate.

The International Phytogenetics Resources Institute (IPGRI), which prepared a checklist to be used during the development of a *sui generis* system, maintains that an appropriate IPR for an industrial system of agricultural production aimed towards export is hardly likely to suit or be appropriate for an agricultural society that is essentially characterised by subsistence. Since both agricultural systems – industrial and subsistence – can be found in the same country, the IPGRI suggests that it would be useful for the countries to study how to associate and harmonise the options, including a ban on double protection and levying different levels of protection for varieties of the same species as per their proposed use.

The appropriateness of a system depends on:

- the type of local seed industry;

- the level of utilisation of the seeds conserved by the farmers;

- the current capacity of the breeders;

- the objectives of the local breeders (national) for the next five to ten years;

- the country's level of advancement in biotechnology;

- the objectives and realistic hopes from the field of biotechnology;

- the kinds of strategic collaborations that could be made.

UPOV a deceptive alternative to patents

UPOV, a multilateral agreement that came into being in 1961, has been adopted by 37 countries, most of which are industrialised. The rights to plant breeding that it promotes were defined to provide exclusive protection to breeders for their intellectual property rights on plant varieties at a time when – before the decision of the US Supreme Court in 1980 – the patenting of living beings was forbidden. During its successive revisions in 1972, 1978 and 1991, the agreement came closer to patent rights in order to cater to the interests of major seed producers. 'The 1991 revision has in fact been conceived in such a way that the UPOV system is almost on par with the patents system,' GRAIN and Gaia point out. For example, whereas the 1978 agreement authorised farmers to keep seeds for their own use, under the 1991 revision 'this right to reuse seeds will be observed only in countries which have included a provision to this effect' (which, of course, is what most member countries did). Another controversial point of UPOV 1991 concerns the rights to the harvest given to the breeder. If the farmer has sown a field with a protected variety without having paid any royalty, the breeder has the right to claim ownership of the harvest as well as the products of the harvest. In addition, this last revision stipulates that the varieties protected by UPOV can also be patented, whereas in the previous versions this double protection was expressly forbidden.

According to GRAIN, UPOV is dangerous not only for farmers but also for biodiversity as it leads to genetic erosion. In order to benefit from UPOV, a variety should fulfil the following three conditions: it should be distinct from all other varieties, present the same characteristics in all successive generations, and all concerned plants should have the same uniform characteristics.

> The criteria of uniformity and stability of the new plant variety make breeders work only with 'élite' genetic material. This signifies that they recycle common improvement material and multiply the variations on a single theme. According to one of the major associations of the improvement industry, less than 7 per cent of the material used by

professional breeders is 'exotic'.... This indicates that no pressure was exerted on plant geneticians to develop varieties with a wider range of genetic diversity. On the contrary, they are encouraged to concentrate on simple genes to differentiate between two distinct varieties. This tendency is very dangerous for farmers. Under the cover of labels and different names, they are offered seeds which are in fact extremely similar. Developing countries are the least suited to bear any loss of harvest that this eroded genetic base could cause.

By encouraging the replacement of genetically broad-based cultivars suited to local conditions with genetically uniform modern varieties, UPOV threatens the biodiversity which is vital for food security in a number of developing countries.

UPOV is not suitable for countries of the South

UPOV is therefore not suited to agriculture in the South. In nearly all the countries of Africa, Asia and Latin America, it is still the farmer or small breeders who breed and improve seeds and not the major corporations on whom the farmers of the North depend. 'The fundamental philosophy of UPOV 91, built on the concept of the right of the breeder, is completely foreign in developing countries,' insists Johnson A. Ekpere.[8]

UPOV grants exclusive rights to breeders and private firms without any recognition of the rights of farmers. The UPOV system fits in perfectly well in industrial economies where the focus is on protecting investments and the interests of major and influential seed companies which employ professional breeders. The situation in developing countries is entirely different. The players in the seed sector and the main producers of seeds are small or cooperative farmers. It is thus obvious that, in these countries, the laws should focus on protecting the rights of these farmers and their interests as breeders or users.... In Africa, for example, as is the case in most developing countries, the role of the farmer in the field is significant. It is he who crosses and breeds plants. Later, he places them at the disposal of other farmers, members of his family and his friends. Generally, it is this pre-selected plant material that scientists procure and introduce in their improvement programmes.... The legislation advocated by UPOV is based on a system where plant breeding is undertaken by private institutions and financed through private funds. Seed companies justify their position of favouring strict IPR because of the huge financial investments that they make. This kind of protection system is understandable in the case of developed countries but it cannot be implemented in developing countries, especially in Africa, due to its low agricultural development.

Beyond these considerations, the basic problem remains: the implementation of UPOV and TRIPS. Both these systems impose exclusively private intellectual property rights on biodiversity which fail to recognise the collective rights of rural communities to this plant heritage, despite the fact that these communities are the main contributors to this heritage. GRAIN and Gaia remind us that

> Most of the cultivated plants come from the South, where the farmers have been breeding, maintaining and preserving agricultural diversity for thousands of years. Their work proved to be one of the greatest contributions to the biodiversity of our planet. The story of the plant varieties that we cultivate and consume today could be described as the most extensive and the most innovative research project in human history. This was recognised by the Convention on Biodiversity, which has legal standing and more signatories than the WTO has members. TRIPS openly goes against the efforts of the Convention to recognise the rights of the farmers and local communities in the South, thereby impeding the very objectives of the Convention.

The Convention on Biological Diversity: a major step forward

What is the CBD? In 1989, UNEP decided to set up a working group to develop an international judicial tool to safeguard biodiversity. It was a strong initiative in reply to an alarming realisation. Never had biodiversity declined so rapidly. Threatened by increased human activity, about 50 to 150 plant and animal species were disappearing every day. Rural communities from countries of the South, which had maintained this biodiversity and depended on it, were also endangered. Their practices and knowledge were declining while at the same time the exploitation of these resources for the benefit of a select few increased. Four years later, in 1992, more than 150 countries (170 presently) signed the CBD at the Earth Summit in Rio. Its main objectives include preserving biodiversity, sustainable use of biodiversity, and fair and equal division of the benefits resulting from the use of genetic resources.

This Convention first recognises the right of sovereignty of each country over its biological and genetic resources (Articles 3 and 15) and stipulates that the access to these resources is subject to 'fully informed prior consent' by the countries concerned (Article 15.5). Second, it demands that its signatories protect and support the rights of communities, farmers and local people to their biological resources and knowledge systems (Article 8(j) and 10). It also calls for equitable sharing of the profits obtained from the commercial use of biological resources and the knowledge of local communities. The main attraction of the agreement perhaps lies in the fact that it finally recognises the significant role that local farmers play in preserving biodiversity. For the CBD, diversity is not just a simple gift of nature but the fruit of the efforts of rural communities. According to it, diversity depends on agricultural practices and ways of life which generate and maintain it. GRAIN and Gaia note that 'The agreement explicitly recognises the intrinsic value of knowledge systems of communities, and it gives more importance to their use and preservation than to the knowledge systems used and marketed by firms.' It is up to the signatory countries to implement and respect the following four commitments: to define the rules that govern access to biological resources; to adopt and apply new systems of rights to protect countries and communities from where biological resources originate; to transfer appropriate technology towards developing countries to help preserve biodiversity; to ensure that the benefits resulting from the use of biological resources (by corporations for example) are shared with communities and populations to whom these resources belong.

An imperfect tool

For many, the Convention can become a useful tool to preserve and use biodiversity if it offers local communities a concrete means of defending their rights against the privatisation of plant varieties. But the CBD is gravely threatened by the implementation of TRIPS, which is diametrically opposed to it. GRAIN and Gaia:

> TRIPS imposes IPR on the biodiversity of countries of the South, whereas the Convention on biodiversity recognises the collective rights of communities to this same resource. The Convention is based on the principle that the local communities generate biodiversity and depend on it, and therefore should continue to benefit from it, whereas the WTO administers worldwide trade, which is to a great extent based on the exclusive private rights of transnational companies as far as biodiversity is concerned.... Since these two instruments contain and suggest conflicting objectives, the legal approaches and contradictory demands of a number of countries raise questions on the precedence of one over the other.

The problem is that TRIPS is more solidly founded than the CBD, perhaps because the American superpower totally supports the agreement on intellectual property rights whereas it has not even ratified the Convention on Biological Diversity. Moreover, TRIPS is one of the three pillars of the WTO, along with trade in goods and trade in services. Geoff Tansey:

> By raising the issue of intellectual property rights and submitting to the settlement procedures of the WTO, the supporters of a strong IPR regime have enabled the imposition of trade sanctions on WTO members in all fields. It could be said that it is essentially for this reason that IPR was vested with the WTO and not with the already-existing World Intellectual Property Organisation. The agreement on TRIPS also includes, for the first time in international law, rules on

national procedures in order to ensure respect of IPR and the corrective measures in this matter.... Conflicts of interpretation are settled by special conflict resolution groups of the WTO and, as a last resort, by the Appeals Board, whose decisions are final and binding. If any country is declared a defaulter as per their interpretations, it must amend its rules or face trade sanctions. If the sanctions in a field covered by an agreement, or in another field, are not applicable, then trans-sectoral trade sanctions could be imposed in fields that are covered in another WTO agreement.

Against this war machine, the CBD can only proffer general principles which are yet to become laws, regulations, decrees or other control systems. Meanwhile a number of points are still to be clarified. How is a local community defined? What is the rate of equitable profit sharing between the company which uses a plant variety and the farmers who contributed to the long process of breeding and crossing?

Now or never

The year 2000 marks a new step in this international legal battle. In conformity with Article 71.1, the TRIPS review should begin this year (that of Article 27.3 (b) started in 1999 but was still in progress at the beginning of 2000). Two questions will be at the heart of the debate: first, excluding the possibility of patenting living organisms; second, a more precise definition of the *sui generis* system.

Excluding the possibility of patenting 'life'

The strategy of most developing countries consists of trying to obtain the exclusion from patentability for plant varieties in the TRIPS agreement. They can no longer be satisfied with the possibility of 'excluding from patentability plants and animals' granted by Article 27.3 (b). They want to see the TRIPS agreement strictly prohibit the patenting of life for all member countries. Johnson A. Ekpere:

> In a workshop where more than 40 trade policy officials from 21 southern and eastern African countries were gathered in Kampala (Uganda) from 4 to 9 March 1999, TRIPS was strongly criticised,

particularly because of the blatant inequalities which present absolute blocks to development in Africa. The participants mentioned several unfavourable consequences such as the constraints on national technological development, blocks against technology transfers, and the surcharges due to monopolies in pharmaceutical products, seeds and software. According to the participants, the most serious problem of introducing TRIPS in Africa is that it does not recognise the rights of local and indigenous communities to their traditional knowledge. Such a situation could lead to the abusive appropriation of their know-how, technology, practices and biological resources by private firms. In anticipation of a re-evaluation of Article 27.3 (b) in the TRIPS agreement, these trade policy officials jointly supported the exclusion of all biodiversity (biological material) from the patents systems.

Since then, the African group has made its official position clear in a statement conveyed to the WTO Secretariat on 29 July 1999: 'The review process should clarify that plants and animals as well as micro-organisms and all other living organisms and their parts cannot be patented.' This is a strong and unequivocal statement.

Guarantees for sui generis systems

The UPOV *sui generis* system is very restrictive. Therefore, many developing countries prefer defining their own system, one which is more in tune with the CBD and grants greater respect to the collective rights of local communities. In Ekpere's account of the meeting where 21 countries from eastern and southern Africa met in Uganda, the officials present

> emphasised that African countries should develop *sui generis* systems for protecting new plant varieties, traditional knowledge and technologies, practices and community rights. These systems should be in line with their national priorities and conform to the objectives of the Convention on biodiversity.

The African group made its intents clear in a statement to the WTO Secretariat in July 1999. The TRIPS agreement 'should specify' that any *sui generis* law for plant variety protection can provide for:

106

> ## An Emergency Exit ?
>
> In case the countries of the South fail to get Article 27.3 (b) revised, they can always bring up section 2 of Article 27 of the TRIPS agreement, which states that
>
> > members may exclude from patentability any invention that might be perceived as detrimental to public order and morality if commercialised on their territory. This includes any threat to human, animal and plant safety or serious prejudice to the environment, provided that such exclusion is not made merely because the commercialisation is prohibited by their national law.
>
> But making use of Article 27.2 will not be easy. The modalities of application are not clear (can it always be proved that an invention is harmful to health or environment?). Moreover, countries which threaten to use this point of the agreement will have to withstand the pressure the American government will not fail to exert in defending the interests of its firms.

1   the protection of the innovations of indigenous and local farming communities in developing countries, consistent with the Convention on Biological Diversity and the International Undertaking on Plant Genetic Resources;

2   the continuation of the traditional farming practices, including the right to save and exchange seeds, and sell their harvest;

3   preventing anti-competitive rights or practices which will threaten food sovereignty of people in developing countries, as is permitted by Article 31 of the TRIPS Agreement.

Clearly, the ultimate objective is to enable states to develop *sui generis* systems that are acceptable to the WTO, that unequivocally recognise the right of farmers to reuse part of their harvest as seeds in the following year without having to pay any royalties, and that protect the knowledge of indigenous and local communities. This protection entails, among other things, the equitable sharing of benefits arising from the commercial use by biotech firms of these knowledge systems and biological resources.

The one and only *sui generis*

But these two stands cannot be defended easily during the TRIPS agreement review. Geoff Tansey:

> The US is in favour of extending the protection given by patents. In the long run, it would like to remove the clause excluding animals and plants from patenting. In the meanwhile, it prefers eliminating the *sui generis* option and introducing UPOV 1991 as the only possibility for protecting new plant varieties. In general, this position has the blessing of the pharmaceutical and agro-biotechnological industries. Most of the other members of the OECD also prefer UPOV 1991 as the only *sui generis* option.

In short, the gap is wide and there will definitely be heated debates between the member states.

If these demands become widely accepted – an outcome on which there is no guarantee – the next step will be to transcribe principles into national laws. Fred Zinanga explains why this task would not be straightforward, either:

> The Community Technology Development Trust (CTDT) together with the Scientific Industrial Research and Development Centre (SIRDC, a government department) have joined hands to develop a *sui generis* legislation on intellectual property rights and patents for Zimbabwe in consultation with relevant government ministries, harmonised through the establishment of an environmental committee. Initial discussions revealed that there was no synergy of the various conventions at the national level. No issue pertaining to the combating of biopiracy had been discussed. In Zimbabwe, the CBD is the responsibility of the Ministry of Mines, Environment and Tourism. TRIPS/WTO falls under the Ministry of Industry and Commerce.

The advocates of *sui generis* who respect the rights of local communities also have to take into account the weight of American trade hegemony. Some countries have already experienced it. Thailand, for example, earned the wrath of the US for expressing its wish to draft a text to recognise its traditional medical knowledge and protect it from being appropriated by major pharmaceutical corporations. According to a Thai group working on farmers' rights, genetic resources and traditional medicine, the American embassy sent a letter to the director general of the Thai Intellectual Property Office expressing the view that this project violates the TRIPS agreement. This is a baseless reproach as the text fits perfectly well within the framework of the CBD and the WTO agreement. But that was much too much for Uncle Sam to bear!

That's why the OAU has drawn up model legislation that should help its members to prepare a *sui generis* system for the protection of new plant varieties and provide a basis for resistance to exterior pressure. The proposed 'African model legislation for the protection of the rights of local communities, farmers and breeders, and for the regulation of access to biological resources' has been formulated through a process of regional and sub-regional consultation that has drawn in selected stakeholders and elicited informed public debate. The draft model legislation was extensively discussed and adopted by a representative group of technical experts from 23 member states in Addis Ababa in November 1999. The objective of the legislation is to give reasoned attention to sustainable agricultural development (food crop and medicinal plant), conservation of biological resources (natural forest products), community rights, equitable sharing of benefits and national sovereignty consistent with the imperatives of the CBD. It is to be hoped that the national legislators will respect the spirit of this project and its helpful legal outline. Now it's up to the voices of public opinion to make themselves heard.

Sui Generis: the Thai Approach

Witoon Lianchamroon of Biothai, the Thai network for the recognition of the rights of local communities and biodiversity, explained the basis on which the new sui generis *system should be adopted in Thailand by the national parliament.*

To date, Thailand does not have any legislation to protect breeders' rights on new varieties, or farmers' rights on traditional varieties.... In 1994, the Ministry of Commerce and the Ministry of Agriculture and Cooperation drafted a plant variety protection bill to protect new plant varieties and the rights of plant breeders. This draft was based on the 1978 version of UPOV and was opposed by Thai NGOs and farmers' networks. Their resistance was grounded in the fact that the draft would not acknowledge the contribution of farmers and local communities to the development of commercial varieties. Eventually, in 1997, the government formed a national committee composed of representatives from all sectors including plant breeders and farmers to redraft the plant variety protection bill.

The present version was drafted to comply with the *sui generis* principles as outlined in Article 27.3 (b) of the TRIPS agreement and was approved by the Thai cabinet. It still needs to be approved twice by Parliament, however, before it can be enforced. The plant variety protection bill is based on the fact that in developing useful plant varieties, local plant varieties are employed as their 'first-hand varieties'. The plant variety protection bill protects the benefits for preservers of local plant varieties as well as owners of commercial plant varieties. Farmers and communities who conserve and improve their seed will have rights to their newly developed plant varieties similar to those enjoyed by plant breeders.

The main principles of the plant variety protection bill are as follows:

- a technical sub-committee will be set up by the Ministry of Agriculture to determine which varieties are specific for certain regions/communities and are therefore considered to be local varieties;

- compensation has to be paid for the use of local plant varieties in the development of new commercialised varieties. The commercial plant breeder must sign a contract which grants at least 5 per cent of the benefits to communities that conserve the original plant varieties. If new cultivars are bred for the benefit of small-scale farmers and local communities or the general public, no compensation has to be paid. Compensation also has to be granted when materials from local plant varieties are extracted to gain ingredients for medicinal or other products;

- rights on plant varieties grown only in particular communities will be enforced only for these communities. The rights to commercial benefits from the varieties will belong to the particular communities for the duration of the protection, which ranges from 15 to 20 years. This rule does not apply if these plant varieties are employed for public or non-profit purposes;

- a new plant variety, especially when it is created by genetic modification, will only be granted variety status if its biological safety is proven. If a new variety causes damage to community environment or community health, its owner, by law, is liable for compensation;

- the purpose of this law – to protect local plant varieties and the rights of farmers and communities – is reflected by the composition of the national plant variety committee. Amongst the 23 members of the committee, there are six farmers and two NGO representatives...;

- the law will establish a foundation for plant variety development and conservation. Income to the foundation arises from different kinds of fees and compensation. It is generated from benefits gained from local wild plant varieties that do not grow in community forests and from local plant varieties which are common assets of many communities. The role of the foundation is to channel the income to the farmers and the local communities. The income will be used for activities in conserving and developing plant varieties in various communities.

... The bill will be effective only within Thailand. It is therefore possible to use Thai plant varieties abroad without complying with Thai plant variety protection law. In this case, the Thai government cannot force a person or organisation to pay for the compensation. In principle, the use of Thai genetic resources outside the country could be regulated by the access regime and benefit-sharing mechanisms that are stated by the Convention on Biological Diversity.... However, the Thai mechanism of compensating local communities will only be possible if Thailand has sufficient bargaining power at the international level.

Notes

1 The patent, issued by one or several countries – and valid only in this or these countries – enables the patent holder to prevent any individual from using his/her 'invention' (a product or a procedure) for commercial activity without authorisation. In exchange for a user's licence, the inventor can ask the user for a fee. After a given number of years (20 in general) the invention falls into the public domain and can be used freely by anybody.
2 Geoff Tansey, 'Trade, Intellectual Property, Food and Biological Diversity; Key Choices and Questions within the Framework of a Re-examination, in 1999, of Article 27.3(b) Dealing with the Agreement on Trade Related Aspects of Intellectual Property Rights (TRIPS)', drafted for the Quaker Committee for Peace and Service, London, February 1999.
3 The *sui generis* system is a system of legal rights adapted to 'inventions' that do not

fall into the traditional categories of protection of intellectual property rights that
include patents and copyrights.

4 GRAIN and Gaia, *World Trade and Biodiversity in Conflict*, Nos 1 and 2, available on
the Internet site of GRAIN: www.grain.org.

5 The first meeting took place in Bangui (Central African Republic), 22–25 February
1999, between the 15 French-speaking countries of the Organisation Africaine de la
Propriété Intellectuelle (OAPI), and the second in Bangkok, 18–19 March 1999.

6 Johnson A. Ekpere, 'An Alternative to UPOV for New Plant Varieties', article distributed during the seminar on 'The Protection of Vegetal Breeding under Article
27.3(b) of TRIPS', jointly organised by UPOV, WIPO and the WTO in Nairobi,
6–7 May 1999.

7 Geoff Tansey, 'Trade, Intellectual Property, Food and Biological Diversity'.

8 Johnson A. Ekpere, 'An Alternative to UPOV for New Plant Varieties'.

CONCLUSION

Rishikesh at the Crossroads

Rishikesh is a place at the intersection of two worlds. It is there that the Ganges – Ganga Ma, mother of Hindu civilisations – leaves the foothills of the Himalayas to flow down to the plains. But Rishikesh is also the meeting point of two types of agriculture. Here, the regular monotony of the large irrigated tracts of the plains gives way to terraces in deep valleys that offer a surprising diversity of farmland. It is in reaction to the progressive replacement of these food crops by monoculture that the farmers created Beej Bachao Andolan – the Save the Seeds movement – close to Rishikesh, in the Garhwal hills. The advance of dwarf varieties of high-yield rice, which have already replaced traditional varieties in the plains, aggravates the dependence of small farmers on chemical inputs without responding to the needs of rural mountain societies for regular and varied food production.

Over several years, the movement for the preservation of local varieties has grown in strength. Its philosophy has spread from village to village across the Himalayan chain. And the movement is now spreading down to the plains where the 'miracle' of the Green Revolution no longer commands belief. The homogeneous high-yielding varieties exhaust the soil and require an increased use of chemical aids – phytosanitary products and fertilisers – that a majority of farmers can no longer buy. The unrelenting economic pressure has led to a spate of suicides among indebted farmers. This issue has received wide coverage in the Indian media. The message of the Save the Seeds movement is reaching the plains on the eve of the advent of

a new era: that of the GMOs, meant to replace and surpass the performance of the Green Revolution. The imminent dangers of the transgenic varieties have accelerated this mobilisation. The Rishikesh
meeting served as a catalyst for collective inter-continental reflection
on the future of rural agriculture confronted with the impact of new
products of the genetico-industrial complex at a time when, for the
first time in India, the test fields of Monsanto cotton were destroyed
and burnt in Karnataka.

The international meeting in Rishikesh led to a final declaration.
Like any statement of principle put forth in a solemn declaration,
Rishikesh might seem abrupt, but it is a well-balanced argument
meant to alert the largest number possible. For some, it might even
appear peremptory or arbitrary, drawn up in ignorance by utopian
old-timers standing in the way of progress. That is why we decided to
unwind the thread of the discussions and set out the arguments that
led us to adopt each of the recommendations that form the mutual
outcome of a melting-pot of world-ranging experiences, reflections
and points of reference.

The recommendations emphasise that the defence of the farmers
must take into account five essential principles :

1 The basic tenet is that seeds belong to farmers. It is not a question
   of demanding a private right to property, but a recognition of pre-
   existing rights of use: the practices of breeding, preservation and
   exchange of seeds ensure food security and the cultural survival of
   rural societies. Besides, this principle guarantees in-depth knowledge of a diversity of farming land and the *in situ* maintenance of
   biodiversity resources for all mankind.

2 It was unanimously agreed that techniques of seed sterilisation by
   genetic engineering should be banned. Used to subjugate farmers
   for the gain of seed suppliers, these Terminator technologies are
   considered treacherous and destructive because they represent a
   danger to the autonomy of farmers' activities and to biodiversity.
   Their proliferation should be compared to biological warfare.

3   The precautionary principle expresses the need for approaching new technologies with prudence. Social control over science has never been more necessary, as an increasing number of indicators confirm the real risks of the large-scale sale of genetically engineered products for health, the environment and food safety.

4   Emphasising transparency aims to fight the lack of appropriate information, insufficiently provided by public institutions. Publicity campaigns orchestrated by GMO export firms and their strategies for putting pressure on scientific and governmental bodies give rise to suspicion about the information that is given. This transparency is deemed necessary to follow the distribution of GMOs between countries and to identify the responsible parties for foreseeable damage.

5   Finally, there is the question of the moral foundations of Western science. What ethical principle permits the development of technologies fraught with new dangers for rural communities and humanity? A science governed and misled by profit is universally reprehensible.

Clearly stated principles, the force of conviction and denunciation are not sufficient. There is an urgent need to initiate global action on legislation by engaging in democratic debate. This is why the participants in the Rishikesh seminar insist on the following points :

6   Citizens' organisations world-wide demand a moratorium on the introduction of GMOs into agriculture and the environment to enable true public debate. This has already been initiated in several countries but needs universal support.

7   In international negotiations to re-evaluate the TRIPS agreement, conducted under the aegis of the WTO, the globalisation of the American right to patent life that issues from biotechnology plays a major role. The private appropriation of genes and genetically modified living organisms places life in the hands of a few multi-

national companies with all the ensuing risks of commercial hegemony. The international community must therefore demand that all living beings be excluded from patenting.

8 On the other hand, it is vital to be able to develop international agreements on trade and *sui generis* systems for the protection of property rights that recognise the rights of agricultural communities over genetic resources that they maintain. This recognition is perfectly in tune with the objectives of the CBD that most countries support.

Since the patenting of life represents a global threat and since multinationals don't recognise boundaries, the citizens of North and South must 'globalise' too – by learning to act as world citizens. The richness of exchange between observers from different continents makes it desirable to have many more international discussions of the kind that took place in Rishikesh, airing the viewpoints of several societies who have experienced this revolution and see it as a threat to their farmers. Strategies of response to questions of great complexity can be defined. Common stands on ethical problems can be formulated which, in their universality, transcend differences and bring together different cultures in a joint battle: protecting life, the common heritage of humanity.

APPENDICES

APPENDIX 1

How to Get More Information

Organizations and internet sites that facilitate research and
distribution of information and debate on the implications
of the advent of GMOs in southern countries

THE EDMONDS INSTITUTE
Conducts research, publishes policy analysis and scientific thought pieces, distributes information, sponsors public workshops, and provides expert
witnesses at national events and for international bodies engaged in decision
making. Disseminates information about and criticism of technology assessment, encourages *pro bono* research and policy analysis by scientists and
scholars, and seeks to create alliances and coalitions with like-minded organisations and individuals. Can put people in touch with other campaigns.
The Edmonds Institute, Beth Burrows, 20319-92nd Avenue West, Edmonds,
WA 98020, USA. Tel.: (425) 775-5383, Fax: (425) 670-8410. [beb@igc.org]
[www.edmonds-institute.org]

RAFI INTERNATIONAL OFFICE
An international non-governmental organisation dedicated to the conservation, sustainability and improvement of agricultural biodiversity, and to the
socially responsible development of technologies useful to rural societies.
RAFI is an important contact for information on patenting, terminator technology, the biotech industry and the loss of genetic diversity, and the relationship of these issues to human rights, agriculture and world food security.
RAFI International Office,110 Osborne Street, Suite 202, Winnipeg, MB
R3L 1Y5, Canada. Tel.: (204) 453-5259, Fax: (204) 925-8034. USA office:
PO Box 640, Pittsboro, NC 27312. Tel.: (919) 542-1396, Fax: (919) 542-
0069. [rafi@rafi.org] [www.rafi.org]

UNION OF CONCERNED SCIENTISTS
Alliance of 70,000 committed citizens and leading scientists who aim to
'augment rigorous scientific research with public education and citizen
advocacy to help build a cleaner, healthier environment and a safer world'.

Provides a critique of the various applications of genetic engineering, and supports sustainable alternatives. Publishes *The Gene Exchange*.
Union of Concerned Scientists, National HQ, 2 Brattle Square, Cambridge, MA 02238-9105, USA. Tel.: (617) 547-5552. [ucs@ucsusa.org] [www.ucsusa.org/agriculture/biotech.html]

GRAIN
Promotes the sustainable management and use of agricultural biodiversity based on people's control over genetic resources and local knowledge, with special emphasis on developing countries. Publish a quarterly newsletter, *Seedling*.
GRAIN, Genetic Resources Action International, Girona 25, pral, E-08010, Barcelona, Spain. Tel : (34) 93 301 13 81 [grain@bcn.servicom.es] [www.grain.org]

CORPORATE WATCH
Aims to document the impacts of transnational companies and supports initiatives for human rights, environmental justice and corporate accountability. Working to harness the Internet as a vehicle for activism.
Corporate Watch, PO Box 29344, San Francisco, CA 94129, USA. Tel.: (415) 561-6568. [corpwatch@igc.org] [www.corpwatch.org]

COUNCIL FOR RESPONSIBLE GENETICS
Focuses on human genetics issues. Also active on biosafety and consumer 'right to know' issues. Produces and distributes educational materials.
Council for Responsible Genetics, 5 Upland Road, Suite 3, Cambridge, MA 02140, USA. Tel.: (617) 868-0870, Fax: (617) 491-5344. [marty@gene-watch.org] [www.gene-watch.org]

THE FOUNDATION ON ECONOMIC TRENDS
Examines emerging trends in science and technology and their impacts on the environment, the economy, culture and society. The President of the Foundation is Jeremy Rifkin, author of *The Biotech Century*.
The Foundation on Economic Trends, 1660 L Street NW, Suite 216, Washington DC 20036, USA. Tel.: (202) 466-2823, Fax: (202) 429-9602. [jrifkin@foet.org] [www.biotechcentury.org]

GREENPEACE INTERNATIONAL
This international ecological organisation conducts awareness and action-oriented campaigns at a global level. Its strategy on GMOs targets four areas: genetically engineered food, artificial organisms, patents on life, and biosafety protocol.

Greenpeace USA, Charles Margulis, c/o Greenpeace GE Campaign, 1817 Gough Street, Baltimore, MD 21231, USA. Tel.: (410) 327-3770. [charles.margulis@dialb.greenpeace.org] [www.greenpeace.org]

INSTITUTE FOR AGRICULTURE AND TRADE POLICY
Aims to create environmentally and economically sustainable communities and regions through sound agriculture and trade policy. Provides educational materials and technical assistance, and works to build networks.
Institute for Agriculture and Trade Policy, 2105 1st Avenue South, Minneapolis, MN 55404, USA. Tel.: (612) 870-0453. [www.iatp.org]

NATIONAL FAMILY FARM COALITION
Leading anti-GE (genetic engineering) farm group in the US. Hundreds of small, family farm member groups throughout the US (mostly in the midwest and New England).
National Family Farm Coalition, 110 Maryland Ave NE, Washington, DC 20002, USA. Tel.: (202) 543-5675.

NATIVE FOREST NETWORK
Working to protect native forests worldwide. Looks at the connections between GE and forestry (e.g., the transnational efforts to bring GE eucalyptus plantations into the rainforest of Chiapas in southern Mexico).
Native Forest Network, NFN/ACERCA, PO Box 57, Burlington, VT 05402, USA. Tel.: (802) 863-0571. [nfnena@sover.net] [www.nativeforest.org]

PESTICIDE ACTION NETWORK (PAN)
Has campaigned to replace pesticides with ecologically sound alternatives since 1982. PANNA is one of five PAN Regional Centers in Africa, Asia/Pacific, Latin America, Europe and North America.
Pesticide Action Network (PAN), North American Office (PANNA), 49 Powell St., Suite 500, San Francisco, CA 94102, USA. Tel.: (415) 981-1771, Fax: 415 981 1991. [panna@panna.org] [www.panna.org]

THIRD WORLD NETWORK
Brings together organisations and individuals involved in development activities and North–South relations. Conducts research on Southern economic, social and environmental issues. Supports call by world scientists for a moratorium on GM crops and the banning of patents. Many publications.
Third World Network, 228 Macalister Road, 104000 Penang Malaysia. Tel: (60) 4 2266728, Fax :(60) 4 226505. [twn@igc.apc.org] [www.twnside.org.sg].

Inf'OGM

Designed as a watchdog on GMOs, Inf'OGM is a non-profit organisation that aims at building up an information service in French for civil society (both associations and individuals) on the debate surrounding the implications of GMOs. Inf'OGM was created in a spirit of 'public service', independently of all parties, technological and financial lobbies, in order to provide the various movements with the core elements of information for an authentic social dialogue. A monthly four-page newsletter is being published.
Inf'OGM, 2b rue Jules Ferry, Montreuil 93100, France. Tel. (33) 1 48 51 65 40, Fax: (33) 1 48 51 95 12.[infogm@altern.org] [http://altern.org/infogm]

PLANET ARK

Planet Ark, an Australian-based NGO with the aim of showing people and business the many ways in which they can reduce their day-to-day impact on the environment, has set up a wonderful service, which, for the moment, is free: the daily Reuters world environment news. The service includes a daily e-mail service of Reuters' environmental headlines with links to the news and an archive that covers the last year and is searchable with boolean operators. Although the service does not cover all Reuters materials, the Planet Ark initiative is most welcome.   [http://www.planetark.org/index.cfm#search]

PERCY SCHMEISER

Once upon our time, a Canadian family farmer, 68-year-old Percy Schmeiser, was unlucky enough to have his field contaminated by Monsanto's RoundUp Ready canola. He was even more unlucky: he had a neighbour who told Monsanto about the presence of this RR canola in his field. Monsanto accused him of patent infringement and demanded restitution for its seeds. Since he denied the accusations, he was brougth to court by Monsanto last August. Schmeiser fought back, launching a $10 million lawsuit that accused the company of a variety of wrongs, including libel, trespass and contamination of his fields with RoundUp Ready. The landmark case, now before the Federal Court of Canada, has attracted international attention because it could help determine how much control a handful of powerful biotech companies can exert over farmers. But Percy Schmeiser needs a good deal of money in order to counter Monsanto's legions of attorneys. In order to obtain economic support for his case, a group of collaborators has established a web page to keep people informed.   [http://fightfrankenfood.com/index.htm]

INTERNATIONAL FORUM ON FOOD AND AGRICULTURE

IFA is a free-standing organisation within the International Forum on Globalisation (IFG), and addresses the global impacts of (industrial) agricultural

production and distribution. Perhaps the best contribution of the site is its resource centre, which includes an electronic library. The library contains the full text of many current and relevant articles on agricultural issues, from biotechnology and agroecology to women in agriculture.
[http://www.ifg.org/IFA/ifa.html/

NATURAL LAW PARTY
The Natural Law Party in Wessex web page keeps an impressive amount of information on genetic engineering. Besides the opinions of the Party, the site contains a useful quotes section on what leading scientists and public figures have said about the dangers of genetically modified foods. Biosafety issues are discussed together with considerations such as the impact on farmers and the real productivity of GM crops. Although the information is stored in an unstructured way and there is no search engine, this web site is really useful for campaigners. They also hold a news listserver that welcomes new subscribers.
[http://www.btinternet.com/~nlpwessex/Documents/nlpwgmo.htm]

SEEDQUEST
The SeedQuest web page is a directory with lots of information on the seed industry, including a list of companies per country and news (press releases) of the last two years. It is not searchable but the information is stored under a very hierarchical system.
[http://www.seedquest.com/]

THE RESEARCH FOUNDATION FOR SCIENCE, TECHNOLOGY AND THE ENVIRONMENT
This foundation has a remodelled web page and a new address. Among the novelties are the online edition of the Biopiracy Factsheet, which also includes transgenic crops and their status in India. There is excellent coverage of Monsanto, which includes the company's illegal field trials in India, its hijacking of Indian public research, and the 'Monsanto, Quit India' campaign. The web site contains the organisation's analysis of biodiversity and biopiracy, food security, globalisation, intellectual property rights, biotechnology, and gender and the environment. It also contains a publications ordering table and the most recent articles by the RFSTE's founder, Vandana Shiva.
[http://writeshop.org/vshiva/]

THE GENETICS FORUM
This UK-based NGO with a long-time involvement in the fight against gene technology and patents on life has set up a new web page, where it introduces itself and lists some of the most interesting articles from its magazine, *The Splice of Life*. The page also contains a calendar of international activities

around biodiversity and genetic engineering. It is still under construction. If
you would like to have links with this web page, go for a visit!
[http://www.geneticsforum.org.uk/]

THE FRIENDS OF THE EARTH EUROPE BIOTECHNOLOGY PROGRAMME

FoEE has for some years closely monitored the political chess game around
GMOs in Europe. Besides introducing their programme and goals, this site
includes the last five issues of the very useful *FoEE Biotech Mailout*. The
organisation was already publishing print and email versions of its *Biotech
Mailout*, and this new outreach is most welcome.
[http://www.foeeurope.org/biotechnology/about.htm]

BIOTECHNOLOGY AND DEVELOPMENT MONITOR

The Department of Political Science, Universiteit van Amsterdam and the
Biotechnology Programme of the Research and Developing Countries
Division, Netherlands Ministry of Foreign Affairs now offer a fully accessible
– and searchable – online version of their publication *Biotechnology and
Development Monitor*. Given the quality of the information provided in this
quarterly, and also its level of analysis of issues ranging from biotechnology to
plant breeding and genetic resources, one can only welcome this initiative.
[http://www.pscw.uva.nl/monitor/index.html

BIOBIN

The Biobin database is a collective effort by the OECD and the United
Nations Industrial Development Organisation (UNIDO). The OECD part
offers a great deal of information: it opens the door to all regulatory bodies on
GMOs in the OECD countries; it contains a field releases database; it has an
ag-biotech products database including companies and genes, which is down-
loadable; it also has consensus documents — amounting to biosafety guide-
lines — for the different crops. The UNIDO part contains the same kind of
information but it is much less comprehensive.
[http://www.oecd.org/ehs/service.htm]

Espa@cenet

The best information source for patent information is Esp@acenet. Searches
European, Japanese and 'worldwide' patent documents. Also provides entry
to European Patent Convention members' patent offices. Full text European
patents since 1996. [http://ep.espacenet.com/]

Part of this list is taken from Luke Anderson's book *Genetic Engineering*, published in the US by
Chelsea Green Publishing Company, PO Box 428, White River Junction, VT 05001. Tel.:
802.295.6300 [www.chelseagreen.com]

APPENDIX 2

Further Reading List

Du Poisson dans les fraises : notre alimentation manipulée.
Arnaud Apoteker, 1999. Editions La Découverte, Paris, 231 pp.
Apoteker takes a comprehensive look at the issues involved in genetic engineering with an emphasis on the scientific and regulatory aspects, and an analytical outlook rooted in the lessons of scientific facts and industrial *realpolitik*.

Gene Wars: the Politics of Biotechnology
Kristin Dawkins, 1999. Seven Stories Press, New York, NY. Site :
http://www.iatp.org/tradeag
Dawkins shows how a diversified gene pool is crucial to food production – and how corporate control of the gene pool threatens our collective security. Behind these issues lies the spectre of globalisation – transnational corporations freely exploiting the resources and consumers of the world while political power shifts to remote international institutions strictly dedicated to commerce. Dawkins challenges those in power to develop global systems of political discourse in the public interest, and shows how each one of us can make a difference.

Global Trade and Biodiversity in Conflict
Series of exposés produced jointly by the Gaia Foundation and Genetic Resources Action International (GRAIN).
'Intellectual Property Rights and Biodiversity: the Economic Myths', No, 3 (October 1998).
'Ten Reasons Not to Join UPOV', No. 2 (May 1998).
'TRIPS versus CBD', No. 1 (April 1998).
All online at www.grain.org
The series examines critical points of conflict between the privatisation of biodiversity, which is being driven by corporate interests and the World Trade

Organisation, and popular efforts to empower local communities in biological and cultural diversity management, particularly in developing countries.

Now or Never. Serious New Plans to Save a Natural Pest Control.
Margaret Mellon and Jane Rissler, 1998. Union of Concerned Scientists.
The report presents new plans to manage the evolution of resistance to *Bt* in transgenic *Bt* corn, *Bt* cotton, and Bt potato. These plans were developed independently by six university scientists, recognised experts in the field of insect resistance. The scientists' recommendations for refuge, sizes, placement and spray choice are intended to be effective options for farmers in conventional systems.

Enclosures of the Mind : Intellectual Monopolies.
A resource kit on community knowledge, biodiversity and intellectual property. RAFI, 1998.
Prepared for the Community Biodiversity Development and Conservation Programme, with the purpose of strengthening the ongoing work of farmers in conserving and enhancing agricultural food security and rural communities. The kit is designed as an information and advocacy tool in response to new, legally binding international agreements: the Convention on Biological Diversity and the GATT administered by the World Trade Organisation.

Appendix 3: Participants, Rishikesh, 5–10 December 1998

Name	Address	Postcode/Town	Country	Tel.	Fax	Email
Ababsa, Faisal Smati	BP 613	30000 Ouargla	Algeria	213 9713039		
Aissaoui Nadia Leila	A6 Neeti Bagh	New Delhi 49	India		91 11 6853819	philippe@nda.vsnl.net.in
Aniruddh, Agnihotri	Disha, Sultanpur Chikan Samaranpur	247 231 Saharenpur	India	91 13 2796224		
Aknak, Nacera	111-2 Rajpur Road	248001 Dehra Dun	India	91 13 5741098		nacera@nde.vsnl.net.in
Apoteker, Arnaud	Greenpeace 21, rue Godot de Mauroy	75009 Paris	France	33 1 53438585	33 1 42665604	arnaud.apoteker@diala. greenpeace.org
Bhattarai, Anil	Marmo Chautari PO Box 4555	Kathmandu	Nepal			yadav@ccsl.com.np
Berrahmouni, Nora	Pnud-Fac 9a, rue Emile Payen	16000 Hydra	Algeria	213 2691212	213 2692355	nora.berrahmouni@undp.org
Brac de la Perrière, Robert Ali	1, rue du Plat	34980 Combaillaux	France	33 4 67 65 45 12	33 4 67 67 06 09	Dombrac@mnet.fr
Cariappa, Vivek	Karnataka Raiya Ravot Sangha KRRS Birwal Village HD Kote Kalu Mysore District	Karnataka	India	8821511144		Glowifil@blr.vsnl.net.in
Cross, Edward	Farmers' Link, Abbey Farm	PE31 6BT Flitcham King's Lynn	United Kingdom			
Dogra Bharat & Madhu	c-27 Rksha Kunj Paschin Vihar	110063 New Delhi	India	91 11 5575303		
Edwards, Cynthia	JPP, Po Bo x 10908	Kathmandu	Nepal	977 1 270466	977 1 259833	jpp@mos.com.np
Guirlet, Philippe	A6 Neeti Bagh	New Delhi 49	India		91 11 6853819	philippe@nda.vsnl.net.in

Name	Address	Postcode/Town	Country	Tel.	Fax	Email
Hammond, Edward	RAFI -110 Osborne Street Suite 202	R3L 175 Winnipeg MB	Canada	1 204 453 52 59	1 204 92580 34	hammond@rafi.org
Heller, Martin	Research foundation for Science, Technology & Ecology	A-60 Hauz Khas New Dehli 110016	India	91 1 1696 80 77	91 1 16856795	hellerm@magellan.colorado.edu
Jaiswal, Rakesh	Eco-Friends, PO Box 287	208001 Kanpur	India	512 405229	512 311356	
Jardhari, Vijay	Beej Bacho Andolan	Naghi–Tehri Garhwal UP 249 175	India			
Kasonia, Kakule	Prelude-SPE 15, rue N. Royer	4367 Fize le Marsal Crisnee	Belgium	32 4 3664175	32 4 3664176	Mansy@ulg.ac.be
Laleye, Issiaka	Sunflower Apts #15 1021 Missouri Street	Lawrence – KS 66044	USA			Iplaleye@falcon.cc.ukans.edu
Lianchamroon, Witoon	Biothai 801/8 Mgamwongwan 27 Soi 5	Muang – Nonthaburi 11000	Thailand			Witoon@vnet.net.th
Louette, Dominique	IMECBIO Av. Independencia Macional 151	48900 Autlan-Jalisco	Mexico	52 33811 425	52 3381165	dlouette@fisher.autlan.udg.mx
Mirenowicz, Jacques	8, place Notre-Dame	1700 Fribourg	Switzerland	41 26 300 86 16	41 26 300 9734	jacques.mirenowicz@icast.org
Muchambo, Peter	APM-Afrique7 PO Box GD 86	Harare	Zimbabwe	263 4 75 70 61	263 4 73 25 85	
Negi Dhum Singh	Beej Bacho Andolan	Naghi–Tehri Garhwal UP 249 175	India			

Name	Address	Postcode/Town	Country	Tel.	Fax	Email
Pionetti, Carine	55, rue Sainte-Catherine	45000 Orleans	France	33 2 38 54 60 80		cpionetti@hotmail.com
Prasun, Kunwar	Beej Bacho Andolan	Naghi– Tehri Garhwal				
Radiu, Jain	Disha Social Org. Sultanpur	Chikana 247 231 Saharanpur (UP)	India	91 3279622		
Ranke, Olivier	1, Grande Rue	95460 Gouzangrez	France	33 1 34677491	33 1 34 6603 23	bergerie@fph.fr
Rao, Vijaya	1464 Poorvanchal	110 057 New Delhi	India			
Ritchie, Neil	IATP 2105 First Av South	55404 2505 Minneapolis	USA	1 612 8703405		Nritchie@iatp.org
Sahu, Suresh	Rupantar A26 Surya Apt	Katora Talab Raipur 492 0010				
Sen, Binayak	Rupantar A 26 Housing Board Complex	Katora Talab Raipur 492 001	India	91 771 42 28 75	91 771 42 79 97	
Singh Jitt, Simron	D 971 Netaji Nagar	110023 New Delhi	India			
Sovani, Manisha	51s/1 Usuf Serai Mahavir Appartments	110 016 New Delhi	India	91 11 619 0777		
Tarradellas, Isabelle	FPH - Longeraie 9	1006 Lausanne	Switzerland	41 21 342 50 10	41 21 342 50 11	lausanne@fph.ch
Tiwari, K.N	Disha Social Org. Sultanpur	Chikana 247 231 Saharanpur (U.P)	India	91 32 79 62 24		
Tjahjadi, Riza	Pan Indonesia J1 Persada raya No. 1 – Menteng Dalam	12870 Djakarta	Indonesia	61 21 829 65 45	61 21 829 65 45	biotani@rad.net.id
Trollé, Arnaud	La Caillère	61100 La carneille	France	33 2 33 96 07 38		
Zinanga, Fred	P.O.Box 7232	Harare	Zimbabwe	263 430 31 60	263 473 36 69	tactdrns@harare.iafrica.com

APPENDIX 4

Report on the Workshop on Genetically Modified Organisms and the Rights of the Rural Community

Saharanpur
10–11 February 1999

A workshop on 'Genetically Modified Organisms and the Rights of the Rural Community' was organised by Disha at its training centre on 10–11 February 1999 after an international workshop with the same title held 5–10 December 1998 in Rishikesh, Dehradun District. There were about 50 participants from different organisations and areas. The report of the Workshop is given below.

First Day, 10 February 1999

First session

Bharat Dogra started the conversation by outlining the objectives and importance of the workshop. He informed farmers about the new genetic technology, terminator seeds, and patent law, as the villagers and farmers did not know about these new words in the context of agriculture. When they were apprised of this technology, they wondered; it was very new and strange information for them. Mr Dogra told that these days multinational companies were trying to make the farmers slaves by producing terminated seeds, pesticides and chemicals by new technology.

The participants were apprised of the new genetic engineering. In this engineering the seeds are treated with some chemicals and become infertile after a specific period. It means that the seeds cannot be used for the next season, cannot be germinated for the future crops. In the coming time these multinational companies will get the rights of production and the farmers will have to purchase seeds by these companies at very high cost. In this way the farmers will become dependent on these multinational companies.

Mr Dogra explained people about patent law. According to this law the production rights will be authorised to big companies and once these companies get the patent law of a particular thing – e.g. turmeric, neem, rice etc. – the farmers cannot produce their own crops, which will be under patent law, e.g. if a company gets the patent of Basmati rice, no farmer can grow that type of Basmati and if he want to grow that type of Basmati he would have to purchase the seeds from that particular company. Patent Law is made by such companies that they just put a small input or charge into the living things or crops and then they own the right of the particular thing.

He told participants about various genetic experiments, as genetic companies are trying to transplant the genes of one animal to the other animal and from one plant to the other plant. He gave an example of Monsanto company; that this company produces those type of pesticides which cannot affect the crop; and the pests growing with the crop will be controlled only by this pesticide. In this way this company is trying to make farmers slave through their own seeds, chemicals and pesticides.

The big multinational companies will bring seeds of high yields but seeds cannot be purchased from any other company, as that company has the patent rights of that particular seed. There should not be the patent of living things. Nobody thought that one day there will be patent of crops and there was only patent of non-living things. As these companies have the patent of things, it is impossible to get the rights in every country of the world as there are more than 200 countries all over the world. Companies put the patent law along with the rules of World Trade Organisation (WTO). In this way the rights of their patent will have to be accepted by every country and thus the patent laws will enter in every country. But the next problem is to supervise the farmers that they use only those seeds which were produced by that company, they brought terminated seeds, the seeds which will not produce the next crop i.e. these seeds cannot be saved for the next time. We can say, the farmers are being put under their control.

He also told that there are some social organisations in developed countries who are worried about the rights of rural community and increasing influence of the big multinational companies. These big countries know the problems of farmers. Some people of rich countries are worried that this type of seed should not go to other countries as it has already badly affected their own country. Having apprised the participants about this technology, terminated seeds and increasing influence of multinational companies over rural community, the farmers were asked to put their thoughts, ideas, reactions on this type of technology.

Mr Sudhir Jain admitted that it is an important issue for Indian farmers, there are big number of Indian farmers who are illiterate and unaware of this technology and in this way it is necessary to make aware our poor and small farmers as well as big farmers. They should be apprised of this new genetic engineering and patent law and its bad effects too. One farmer gave a general example that in olden days when people got fever they were given the home-made domestic medicines. These medicines made patient good within few days but nowadays fever cannot be controlled through these home-made medicines and we have to buy English allopathic medicines, which are very expensive. In this way these big companies think only their own profit. They do not think about the betterment of people.

Disha's director Mr K. N. Tiwari expressed his reactions that these big multinational companies like Monsanto help government and very easily they got power. Mainly rich farmers accept this technology as financially they are very strong and can use new technology but the bad effects of GMOs will affect the whole agriculture. Beside this there are few such farmers too who worry about the rights of rural community and they protest against GMOs. Mr Arun Kumar the farmer and Disha's worker expressed his worry; he said that urea had become very essential for soil. We cannot get a good yield without using urea and every year the soil needs more and more urea and due to this the soil texture becomes weaker day by day.

Another farmer Mr Rampal said that these days the farmers are dependent on chemicals, pesticides and due to which the fertility of the soil is being very weak. As the crops which are produced from a lot of chemicals and pesticides are the main cause of new diseases. The seeds which produce high yield needs more fertiliser and pesticides, but on the other hand the farmers have to spend more money to purchase fertilisers and chemicals. So he is not in profit and also loses the fertility of his soil. Another farmer expressed his feelings about genetically modified organisms. According to him farmers should use their own seeds and natural compost. They should not get attracted by window dressing of big multinational companies. They should save their local traditional seeds.

A farmer coming from adjacent village expressed his reaction that in olden days we plough the field by bullocks and oxen and used our old traditional seeds and compost produced from debris and other residues, but these days it is necessary for us to use new seeds, fertilisers and pesticides but these are more expensive and make our produce/crops more costly. The nature of the agriculture field is so, if we apply 10 kg of urea in one year it will be necessary to apply 15 kg in the next year for the same crop and same result. We are applying pesticides year by year so fruit trees are affected and if we don't apply pesticide in any year the trees don't give good production. By the use of these pesticides they lose their natural taste and become more toxic. The farmers and orchard owners have no proper education about pesticides so they have no idea how many days and months these pesticides remain effective.

According to Mr Harichand by using English pesticides and fertilisers the soil is losing its natural fertility. A government servant of Agriculture Department Mr Babu Wazid said, 'We are applying chemical fertilisers and producing crops year by year the yield is decreasing after it. If we apply natural compost fertiliser we received higher yields.' Another participant said that we were losing our traditional seeds and moving towards hybrid seeds and chemically treated seeds. Many crops like *samak* are nearly extinct.

If we use traditional seeds we need not use any chemical fertiliser; if we apply them the seedlings (plants) made an extraordinary growth and falls down. These indigenous crops are so popular that even an uneducated person demand for these local traditional produces in the market. Mr Yashvir said that we are using cropping pattern rice–wheat–sugar cane. If we change our cropping pattern and grow some intermediate crops then it will be more profitable to villagers. When an insect affects a tree, we use pesticides on the tree but by the use of pesticides some friendly insects also get killed – e.g., the earthworm who make our soil fertile, cannot survive.

Mr Dogra remarked our farmers are real scientists. They have lot of experience to know the beneficial insects, the insects which help farmers. He gave example of Mr Richariya. According to him, green revolution was not good for farmers, and due to this attitude he was compelled to resign from his post. In this way, a scientist who told about the bad effects of green revolution, was given an unexpected reward.

Second session

Mr Kunwar Prasun, a senior activist of Beej Bacho Andolan (Save Our Seeds campaign) in Garhwal hills, shared his experiences and expressed his reaction on new genetic technology and patent law. He was worried about the traditional agriculture, nowadays every farmer is running towards hybrid seeds and forgetting his traditional seeds and fertiliser. According to him the coming time would be dangerous for our agriculture. He expressed that in coming days when farmers would be compelled to use terminated seeds and then they would have to purchase those seeds for every season at very high cost.

He urged farmers not to run after new hybrid seeds and to save their local traditional seeds so that they should not face the problem in future. He was also worried about the disappearing of old local traditional seeds. The new hybrid seeds give high yields in beginning but every next time the production decreases and more chemicals, fertilisers and pesticides are needed. He told about the old varieties of rice which produced high yield without applying any chemical fertiliser. New hybrid varieties need more chemical fertilisers and due to which natural fertility of the soil gets weak.

He gave example of *Jharai*, a variety of rice, this variety grows well at 1500 metre altitude and it is not affected by hailstorm or cold. There were nearly 200 traditional varieties of rice and many of them had high yield but farmers did not save seeds and today many varieties have disappeared. In hill areas they did great efforts to mobilise farmers to save seeds and now people are saving their traditional seeds. They are also using compost and manure to increase the fertility of the soil.

He requested the participants to mobilise farmers through campaigns and meetings so that farmers can save their traditional seeds and ignore the new hybrid seeds. He also told that there were nearly 200 known varieties, but today there are only 120 varieties in practice. During the campaigns they exchanged hybrid seeds to the old traditional seeds and farmers exchanged their hybrid seeds and got old traditional seeds.

According to him there were nearly 40 varieties of traditional wheat seeds out of which only 6 are of dwarf variety. He felt that farmers should use multi-cropping system instead of single cropping system. In this system two or more than two different crops can be grown simultaneously. He emphasised to protest against patent law. According to him a proper strategy should be adopted to mobilise and organise people against the patent law and genetic engineered seeds.

Another participant from Beej Bacho Andolan was Mr Dhum Singh Negi, the activist of Chipko Movement. He also reacted against the genetically modified organisms. He was agreed with the views of Mr Prasun. He said that these multinational companies were trying to make farmers dependent on them and wanted to keep the farmer under their rule.

The aim of these companies is to get more and more profit, as there is a big competition among them and they want to hold a big part of the agriculture. They have nothing to do with farmers. The farmers of different region grow different crops, as in hill areas people grow *Mandwa* and *Baranaja*. He also said that there were some insects who helped farmers in different ways. The earthworm makes the soil fertile, but when farmers apply chemicals to the crop these helpful creatures die. According to him people should not compromise on the cost of their soil and seeds because this new technology and patent law can ruin their traditional agriculture.

After the expressions of the participants there was an open discussion, in which farmers put their views and suggestions. According to Mr Rahtulal today every farmer needs more and more yield and to get high yield he uses high quantity of fertilisers and chemicals but actually he ruins his own field by applying chemicals. Today farmers use very costly fertilisers and pesticides to get better crop but there is not a good profit as the cost of maintenance of the crop becomes equal to the selling price of the crop and the crop and fruits becomes more toxic by using chemicals. He told about the old traditional varieties of rice such as *Latthmar, Lalmati, Bindli* and *Gundhi*. These varieties give high yields without using chemical fertilisers. These days people grow dwarf varieties which don't produce fodder for the cattle.

Mr Rampal, a farmer, agreed with Mr Rahtulal. He told that in olden days villagers had large number of cattles and through cattle they get dung manure for their fields and there was no need of applying chemical fertilisers, but these days people use chemicals and fertilisers due to which soil is getting infertile and the taste of the fruits and grains is getting more toxic in nature. He told about few old traditional varieties of wheat, e.g. *Turak, Murak*. These varieties of wheat are very useful and should be saved. He said that we should make efforts to mobilise and organise the rural community on the issue of Terminator technology and for this we have to make a proper strategy along with organisations.

After the talk of Mr Rampal, Mr Prasoon and Mr Dhum Singh Negi sang a Garhwali song and other participants followed them and then workshop was adjourned till the next day.

Second day – 11 February 1999

First session

Mr Bhoop Singh expressed his reactions. He told that today's farmer does not think about the soil. He applies more and more fertilisers to the soil and as a result the soil texture is getting weaker day by day. He worried that small marginal farmers sell their fields to rich farmers at very low price because they are unable to earn their livelihood through small pieces of land. Big and rich farmers take their fields at very low prices and use the land for their unfair business.

Mr Yogendra, a farmer, told about the border area of two districts, Madhya Pradesh and Uttar Pradesh, that there are number of small farmers who have not more than half acre of land per farmer. They have nothing to do with the small pieces of land. They have no resources to do agriculture and they depend on rainwater only to irrigate the fields. So there is a need to make fields available on lease with the help of the administration.

He explained people how to make the compost. In this process small pits are dug and filled with debris and other residues. These debris and residues are mixed to make the soil fertile. According to his experiment he selected three fields. The first field was applied chemical fertiliser. The second field was treated with wormy compost and the third one was applied compost and cow dung manure. When he got the vegetables from three different fields he found that the vegetables from second and third fields had good taste as compared to the vegetables from the first field. In this way he concluded that chemicals and fertilisers make the soil infertile, grains and fruits tasteless. The compost is cheaper than chemical fertiliser and another fact is that we cannot apply the fertiliser in unirrigated fields while compost can be applied to unirrigated fields.

Mr Rampal said that a few years ago people cultivated the eucalyptus and this plant makes the soil infertile as it needs a much higher quantity of water so the soil becomes infertile, but these days people cultivate poplar (its wood is used to make matchsticks and ply, etc.). This plant is very useful and doesn't need a higher quantity of water. Its leaves fall and make the soil fertile. Today a large number of farmers cultivate this plant and it is also a cash crop. The other thing is that we can grow another crop along with this crop and it is not harmful for the other crop.

All the participants were agreed that new genetic technology and patent law are not suitable for small farmers as well as rich farmers and every farmer should protest against patent law, terminated seeds and its technology. According to the participants all these things hurt the rights of the rural community. They also hoped that the government would not compromise with these big multinational companies and would save the rights of the rural community.

Beside this, participants were worried about division of fields among the family members which causes small pieces of land. The farmers cannot get their livelihood through small pieces of land. Participants put a few suggestions to work on this issue:

1 The rich families who live in big cities and earn thousands of rupees per month they should not be the owner of thousands of acres in rural areas. This type of land should be leased to small and marginal farmers.

2 There should not be the contract pattern in agriculture and small farmers should cultivate their fields themselves.

3 Small farmers should not sell their valuable fields to rich hands.

4 The laws relating to land should be enacted severely and big farmers who have thousands of acres of land want to put small farmers under their control by buying their fields at very low prices.

5 The government should think about the betterment of farmers and rural community before signing any agricultural agreement.

6 People should use natural compost and manure and local, traditional varieties of seeds.

Mr Bhatt from UPVAN said that we had to make a common strategy to mobilise and organise small and big farmers on this issue. We have to organise a few agriculture scientists to help in traditional agriculture. According to him government policies often ignore the rights of the rural community and due to this farmers face loss. He gave an example of government policy. During the 1960s there was a state agriculture minister who encouraged the work of making pits to make compost on block level. When the reports reached him from the blocks, the total area of the pits was greater than the area of the state, which was a very interesting fact. It was an example of false reporting.

He said that UPVAN would like to organise the state's defences against genetic technology and patent law. According to him, if we save soil, we save environment; otherwise it would be dangerous in coming days. Disha should drive campaigns to mobilise and organise the rural community along with the local participants in this workshop.

According to Mr K. N. Tiwari, the director of Disha, we have to organise the groups who hold the same views on this important issue. We have to make an effective strategy against genetically modified organisms. He said that the previous workshop was organised in Rishikesh on the same issue and participants in that workshop had identified the need to drive a world-wide campaign against GMOs and this type of technology.

At the end of the workshop participants were agreed on the following points:

1 Campaigns should be driven to inform people about genetically modified organisms and Terminator technology.

2 People should use their local traditional seeds.

3 People should abate the use of chemical fertilisers and pesticides as they are slow poison for humankind.

4 There should not be a contract pattern in agriculture.

5 Small and marginal farmers should not sell their valuable fields to rich farmers.

INDEX

quality characteristics introduced
33-4; and new viruses 49;
pesticide reduction claimed for
42-3, 63; planetary scale of
problem 68; political control of
79; pollution by irreversible 82-
3; poor countries as laboratories
18; precautionary principle on
38-52, 84-5; prices hit by 16, 19;
principle of challenged 77; properties of 2; public rejection of 66;
rapid development by multinationals 39-40 82, 84; regulation
of 18, 84-5; and relief of world
hunger 56-62, 84; research on
86-8, 95; resistance to antibiotics
of 48-50, 83; Rishikesh seminar
on 3-5; risks of 56, 86; and rural
communities 4, 15, 45-7, 79,
130; salinity-resistant 58; secrecy
over 5, 56, 62-5, 73, 95; stock
market signals 41; superweeds
and 45-6; Swiss referendum
opposes Brussels on 4; toxicity of
47-8; trade in 50, 75, 103; trials
of 5; uncertainty of 83; uniformity of 1-2; worst yet to come?
32; see also genetic engineering,
Terminator gene
genetico-industrial complex 27, 114
Genetics Forum 123-4
Germany 84
globalisation 13, 91
Greece 85
green revolution 1-2, 13, 45, 58-61,
113-14, 133
Greenpeace 13, 68, 120-1; France 9,

38, see also Apoteker, Arnaud
Guirlet, Philippe 128
Gulf of Mexico 15
Gumi 60

Hammond, Edward 62, 64, 128
Harichand, Mr 132-3
health hazard 5-6, 18, 28, 30, 38-40,
47-52, 56, 64, 81-3, 85, 110,
115
Heller, Martin 128
herbicide1, 13, 16, 29, 33, 41-2, 51,
57, 59, 68, 72, 74
Himalaya mountains 61, 113
Hoechst 11, 72
Hoffmann, José Hermero 18
Horsch, Robert 57
human genes 20
hunger 14, 21, 56-9, 62
hybrids 26-7, 34-5, 46

India 32, 45, 61, 82
Indonesia 19
industry 14, 75
Inf'OGM 121-2
informed consent 20
insecticide 51, 133-4
Institut National d'Agronomie Paris
Grignon 19
Institut Panos 19
Institute for Agriculture and Trade
Policy (IATP) 12-13, 44, 57, 87,
121; see also Ritchie, Neil
Institute of Science, Technology
and Ecology 82
intellectual property rights 9, 22, 73,
89-111; see also TRIPS

THIS BOOK IS AVAILABLE IN THE FOLLOWING COUNTRIES:

FIJI
University Book Centre
University of South Pacific
Suva

Tel: 679 313 900
Fax: 679 303 265

GHANA
EPP Book Services
PO Box TF 490
Trade Fair
Accra

Tel: 233 21 773087
Fax: 233 21 779099

INDIA
Segment Book Distributors
B-23/25 Kailash Colony
New Delhi

Tel: 91 11 644 3013
Fax: 91 11 647 0472

MOZAMBIQUE
Sul Sensacoes
PO Box 2242
Maputo

Tel: 258 1 421 974
Fax: 258 1 423 414

NEPAL
Everest Media Services
GPO Box 5443, Dillibazar
Putalisadak Chowk
Kathmandu

Tel: 977 1 416 026
Fax: 977 1 250 176

PAPUA NEW GUINEA
Unisearch PNG Pty Ltd
Box 320, University
National Capital District

Tel: 675 326 0130
Fax: 675 326 0127

RWANDA
Librairie Ikirezi
PO Box 443,
Kigali

Tel/fax: 250 71314

TANZANIA
TEMA Publishing Co Ltd
PO Box 63115
Dar es Salaam

Tel: 255 51 113608
Fax: 255 51 110472

ZAMBIA
UNZA Press
University of Zambia
PO Box 32379
Lusaka

Tel: 260 1 290 409
Fax: 260 1 253 952